SDK228 The science of the mind:
investigating mental health
Science: Level 2

Book 2
Mood and Well-being

This publication forms part of the Open University course SDK228 *The science of the mind: investigating mental health*. The complete list of texts that make up this course can be found at the back. Details of this and other Open University courses can be obtained from the Student Registration and Enquiry Service, The Open University, PO Box 197, Milton Keynes MK7 6BJ, United Kingdom (tel. +44 (0)845 300 60 90; email general-enquiries@open.ac.uk).

Alternatively, you may visit the Open University website at www.open.ac.uk where you can learn more about the wide range of courses and packs offered at all levels by The Open University.

To purchase a selection of Open University course materials visit www.ouw.co.uk, or contact Open University Worldwide, Walton Hall, Milton Keynes MK7 6AA, United Kingdom for a brochure (tel. +44 (0)1908 858793; fax +44 (0)1908 858787; email ouw-customer-services@open.ac.uk).

The Open University, Walton Hall, Milton Keynes MK7 6AA

First published 2010

Edited and designed by The Open University.

Typeset by The Open University

Printed and bound in the United Kingdom by Bell & Bain Ltd, Glasgow

The paper used in this publication is procured from forests independently certified to the level of Forest Stewardship Council (FSC) principles and criteria. Chain of custody certification allows the tracing of this paper back to specific forest-management units (see www.fsc.org).

ISBN 978 1 8487 3546 0

1.1

Contents

Chapter 1 Sadness and anxiety: emotions and emotional disorders

Saroj Datta

1.1 Introduction to mood and well-being

In this book, Chapters 1–3 focus on disorders related to sadness and anxiety. You will build on the knowledge and understanding you have gained from Book 1 about how disorders are diagnosed, their correlates and possible causes, and the kinds of help available to people with such disorders. In addition, Chapter 1 looks at how emotions and emotional disorders can be placed in the wider context of our evolutionary heritage.

Following on from these chapters, Chapter 4 focuses on positive emotions such as happiness, and considers the important question of what constitutes and promotes emotional well-being.

1.2 Moods, emotions and disorders

1.2.1 What is an emotional disorder?

Depression (also known as **major depression** or **MD**) is the most commonly occurring of a set of mood disorders known as **affective disorders**, 'affect' being another term for 'mood'. Most of us have experienced low mood, unhappiness, sadness or depression at some point. Recall Neha, whom you met in Book 1, and who fell into deep depression following a sequence of stressful life events.

A set of disorders often distinguished from affective disorders is **anxiety disorders**. These have in common a strong element of fearfulness, apprehension or anxiety and include **generalised anxiety disorder (GAD)**, panic disorder, phobias, and obsessive–compulsive disorder (OCD), which caused John and Stacey much distress (Book 1). Anxiety and affective disorders are collectively often referred to as **emotional disorders**, and this is the term that will be adopted in this book. (See Box 1.1 for a clarification of terminology relating to such disorders, and Box 1.2 for terminology relating to moods and emotions more generally.)

Box 1.1 A note on terminology

The terminology used to classify mental health disorders has developed and changed over many decades. Multiple usages are current and can be confusing. 'Affect' is another term for 'mood', so 'affective disorders' refers to 'mood disorders'. These are distinguished from 'anxiety disorders'.

'Affect' can also mean 'emotion' – so 'affective disorders' is also used as a term for 'emotional disorders'. It may puzzle you that 'affective disorders' do not include anxiety disorder(s), even though anxiety is certainly an emotion! This is simply an anomaly rooted in the history of terminology in this area.

Affective and anxiety disorders were once lumped together as '**neurotic disorders**', and are occasionally still referred to as such. This usage comes from the definition of '**neurotic**': a person who is neurotic is 'emotionally unstable or unusually anxious'. Anxiety and affective disorders are also called 'common mental disorders' or emotional disorders (from the *Adult Psychiatric Morbidity in England, 2007: results of a household survey* (APMS 2007) (McManus et al., 2009)).

Box 1.2 Moods, emotions, states and traits

So far in SDK228 you have come across mention of moods (for instance, 'low mood' – Book 1, Chapter 1) and emotions, and may have wondered whether or not different things are meant by these two terms.

In fact, there is no real consensus on this issue. Mood, like emotion, is an affective state. Those in favour of a distinction suggest that emotion has a clear focus (i.e. its cause is self-evident), whereas mood is diffuse and can last for days, weeks, months or even years.

Other researchers use the terms 'emotion' and 'mood' interchangeably. The basic disagreement seems to be about whether it is important to recognise that one state (emotion) is normally associated, by the person experiencing it, with a particular object or cause, and the other (mood) is often not. What difference might this make? Some evidence suggests that a particular 'mood' can affect our thoughts, perceptions and behaviours for prolonged periods – the so-called 'mood effect'.

There is evidence that when a mood or its source is brought to the attention of the person experiencing it, the mood effect can disappear (Schwarz, 1990). So it has been suggested that although moods (like emotions) can have identifiable sources, the effects of moods depend on the sources going unnoticed; and that a distinction between moods and emotions is therefore meaningful and even useful.

Certainly, it may help our understanding of some kinds of treatment for affective and anxiety disorders (Chapter 3). For instance, mindfulness-based or cognitive therapy approaches may exert their effect by training people to become more aware of their moods, and of what is influencing or causing them.

Another common distinction found in the study of moods and emotions concerns states and traits. A **trait** is a relatively stable attribute of an individual, whereas a **state** is a temporary response to circumstances.

Take, for example, anxiety. A person shows **state anxiety** when something causes him or her to feel anxious temporarily. The anxiety then dissipates and the person feels 'normal' again. But in some people anxiety is a trait – they can be described as 'anxious people'. **Trait anxiety** has been suggested as a relatively stable characteristic of a person.

While traits may be more stable, it does not mean that they are not malleable, at least to some extent, though perhaps they are harder to change.

1.2.2 Occurrence and cost of emotional disorders

There are good reasons for choosing depression and anxiety disorders as our first point of focus within SDK228. Whilst anxiety and sadness are everyday emotions, their more serious manifestations can be hugely problematic for a significant number of people.

National statistics compiled by the Government show that in England in 2007, 16.2% (around 1 in 6) of 7325 adults between the ages of 16 and 64 years met the diagnostic criteria for at least one emotional disorder (or common mental disorder; McManus et al., 2009).

Of these, depression and anxiety (or a mix of the two, called mixed anxiety and depression or MAD) were by far the most common, as Figure 1.1 shows.

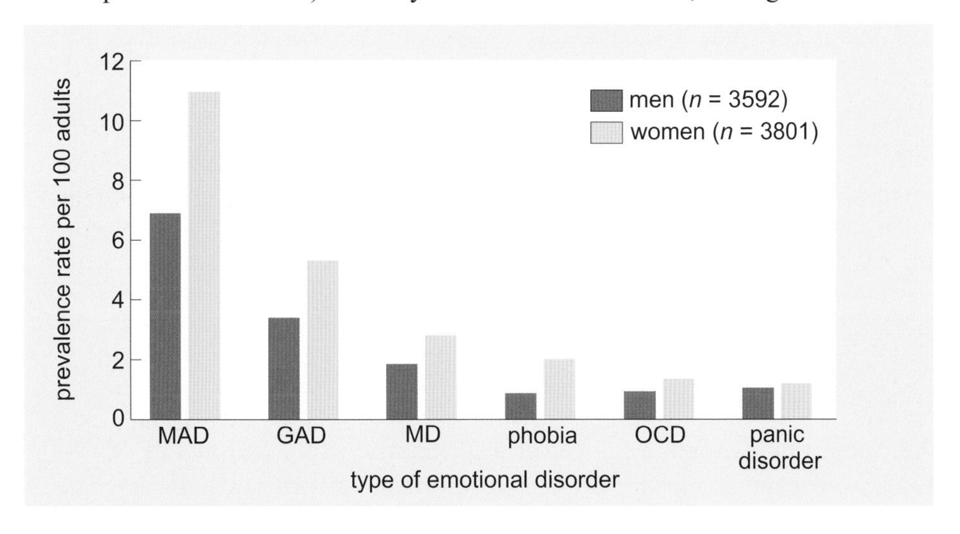

Figure 1.1 Prevalence rates in England in 2007 of a range of emotional disorders (also known as common mental disorders) by gender. MAD: mixed anxiety and depression; GAD: generalised anxiety disorder; MD: major depression; OCD: obsessive compulsive disorder.

■ Why do we consider that the data in Figure 1.1 show prevalence *rates* and not prevalence?

□ Because they show the number of people who have emotional disorders, expressed as a *rate* per 100 (i.e. percentage) of the population. Prevalence would just tell us the *total number* of people with emotional disorders in the population (Book 1, Section 4.2.5).

The burden to society as a whole is considerable, as anxiety and depression are implicated in 20% (1 in 5) of days lost from work in Britain, and around one in five GP consultations in the UK are about emotional disorders.

Depression has been linked to the loss of more than 100 million working days in England every year, and it is strongly associated with suicidal thoughts and with suicide, being implicated in around 2500 deaths a year (Thomas and Morris, 2003). McCrone et al. (2007) estimated the total annual cost of depression, including lost employment, in England as at least £7.5 billion a year.

Clearly, it is important to try to understand both emotions and emotional disorders. We start by looking at the nature of emotions and emotional systems.

1.3 Emotions in an evolutionary context

Like other living things, people are the products of millions of years of evolution. The evolutionary stance thus has the potential to provide a number of important insights into the nature and function of emotions and emotional systems, and to enhance our understanding of what constitutes mental health and ill-health (Marks and Nesse, 1994; Nesse, 2006).

The evolutionary stance postulates that many of our physical, mental, social, emotional and spiritual characteristics and tendencies exist because they were useful or even essential in enabling our ancestors to survive and reproduce more successfully than their competitors. In other words, such characteristics and tendencies were **adaptive**.

It is also important to realise that evolutionary processes build on, or modify, what is already there – they cannot start from scratch. The changes brought about by evolution are a bit like remodelling your home over time. You may have installed electricity in your ancient cottage, but the low beam at the bottom of the stairs is part of the core structure of the building and cannot be removed. So, though you need to bend a bit to avoid banging your head on it, you just have to live with it.

In the same way, we retain a great deal of the machinery and modes of operation of many of our ancestors. For instance, parts of our brain have a similar structure and organisation to that of many other animals.

1.3.1 The universality of emotions

The evolutionary stance suggests that non-human animals, our evolutionary relatives, experience emotions too. Anybody who has a pet dog or has observed any animals carefully should need no convincing of this! Charles Darwin was one of the first to study the expression of the emotions in animals and humans systematically (Darwin, 2009 [1872]). Figure 1.2 shows a dog expressing two rather different emotions – aggression and fearfulness (or submission).

- Look carefully at the two pictures of the dog and list the main differences you can see between the aggressive and the fearful postures.

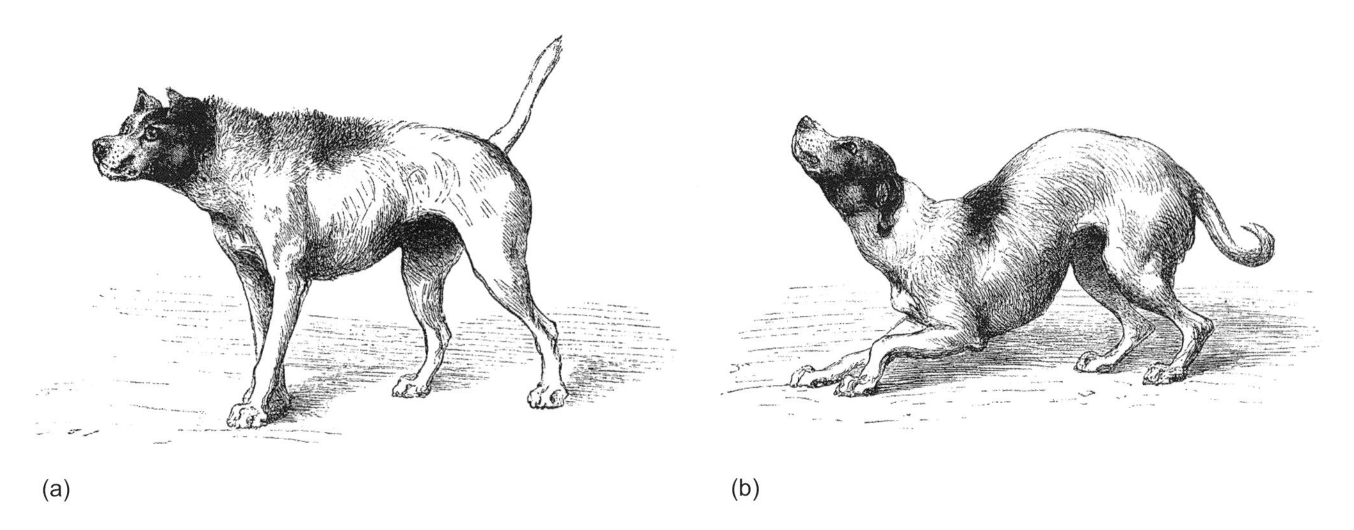

Figure 1.2 Dog showing (a) aggressive and (b) submissive posture.

□ The position of the ears, the tail and the height of the body are all different. The aggressive dog stares straight ahead; the submissive dog does not. The hairs on the back of the aggressive dog are raised. You may have noticed other differences too.

It is striking how different the postures are. Indeed, diametrically opposite emotions appear to have evolved features that make it easy to tell them apart. Similarly, a happy face is normally easy to distinguish from an angry one (Figure 1.3). Such features suggest that the expression of emotions has an important function in social communication – for instance, in letting others know how we feel and what the consequences, pleasant or unpleasant, might be if they approach us.

A consequence of the evolutionary heritage we share with other animals, in particular mammals such as rats, and even more so, monkeys and apes, is that there is significant similarity in the biological bases of many of our emotional response systems, as you will see in Section 1.3.2.

The evolutionary stance also suggests the universality of human emotions – an idea again first clearly espoused by Darwin (2009 [1872]). This is the idea that all human races and cultures experience similar emotions, such as sadness, anger and joy. This has not always been accepted, which is not surprising, as cultural differences amongst humans have created strikingly different behaviours and displays of emotions in circumstances that appear otherwise comparable. A classic example is provided by cultural differences in the public expression of emotion at the death of a loved one. In traditional Japanese culture, weeping and wailing in public would be deemed scandalously uncontrolled and undignified. In others (such as traditional Indian culture), the absence of such behaviour might be deemed equally scandalous – signifying a lack of feeling for, and attachment to, the deceased.

Differences such as these led to the assumption that people in different cultures did not feel the same emotions, or did not feel them in the same way (e.g. Bruner and Tagiuri, 1954). However, there is convincing evidence of the universality of basic human emotions. Paul Ekman and his colleagues

(Ekman, 1972) showed photographs of North Americans displaying a range of emotional expressions to people, such as the Fore of New Guinea, who had had virtually no contact with Westerners. They wanted to know which expressions the Fore would identify as (say) those of a man who had lost his child.

- ■ Why was it important that the Fore people had had minimal contact with Western culture?
- □ To ensure that they had not simply learned about the relationship between the expressions in the photos and the emotions that the photos represented, via contact with Western culture.

The Fore did prove competent at identifying emotions in Western faces. Ekman and his colleagues also photographed responses to emotional situations in the Fore, and this time asked North Americans to assess them – which they did, also accurately. Ekman concluded that recognition and expression of emotions was shared across cultures, at least for the six emotions he felt were 'basic': happiness, surprise, sadness, anger, fear and disgust; see Figure 1.3.

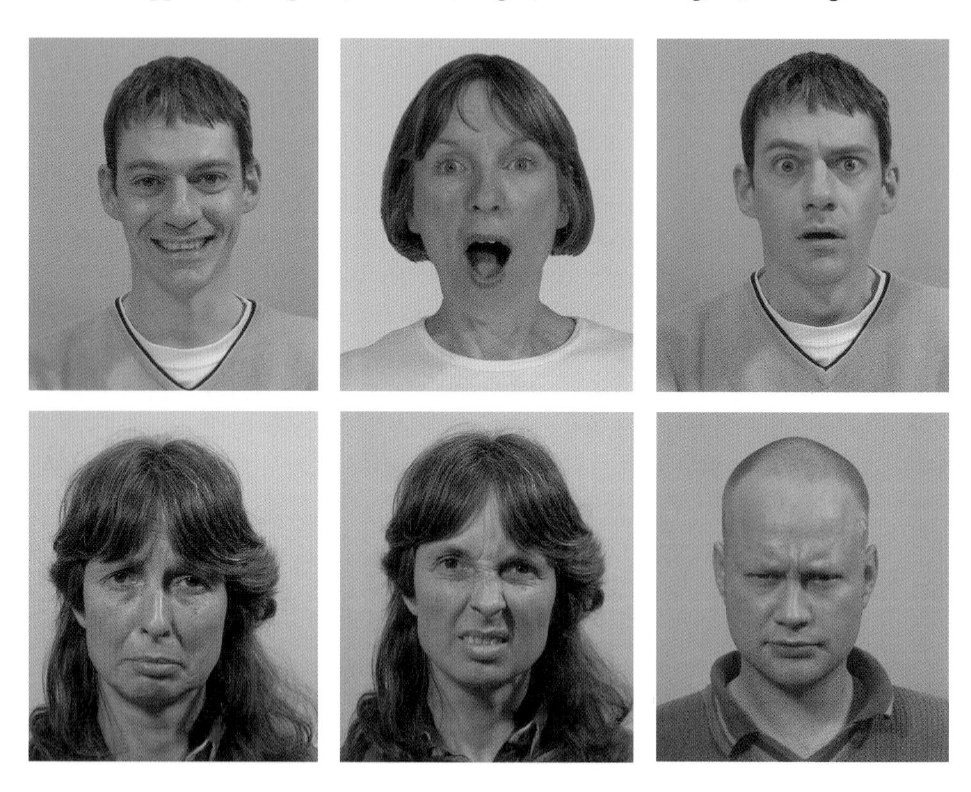

Figure 1.3 Photographs showing facial expressions for the six basic emotions. Top row, left to right: happiness, surprise, fear. Bottom row, left to right: sadness, disgust, anger.

But explanation was still needed for the fact that people from different cultures sometimes showed different expressions in circumstances where one would expect them all to show a particular emotion, such as sadness. Ekman suggested that this was because different cultures learned different 'display rules' for emotions. For instance, Japanese culture has a display rule that emotions such as anger or disgust must not be expressed in front of people of higher social status, whereas North American culture does not have such a rule. When Japanese and Americans were secretly observed watching a gory film, both showed facial expressions of disgust. When they were shown the film in the presence of a person with higher social status, the Japanese smiled, but the Americans still showed facial expressions of disgust.

Based on such findings, Ekman (1972, 2003) proposed his **neurocultural theory of emotions**. This suggested that certain human emotions were universal, but that the facial expression of these emotions could be influenced by social learning via local culture.

'Culture' is used here to mean practices or ways of thinking, so the term can apply widely, at different levels. Thus there could be 'cultural' differences between socio-economic classes, between men and women, and so on.

All in all, therefore, sadness and anxiety have the same biological bases in all humans, and are experienced in fundamentally similar contexts – thus bad feelings are reliably aroused by losses, threats of losses, and the inability to reach important goals (Emmons, 1996).

However, culture does have an effect. It can affect *what* we regard as important goals or losses and therefore what triggers our emotions. Thus, in Westernised societies, some women may feel anxious and depressed at not being as thin as their culture considers desirable. In some Asian cultures, where male offspring are greatly prized, some women who give birth to one daughter after another may feel great despair and anguish. Cultural factors may also come into play in how acceptable people find it to display emotions and to admit to feelings, particularly negative ones. As diagnosis of emotional disorders is reliant on subjective report and assessment by interviewers, it is easy to see how cultural factors could impact on the diagnosis of problems like depression and anxiety (Section 1.5.1; see also Book 1, Section 4.2.6).

Our basic emotions, however, are those that all humans feel, and underlying them are brain structures and connections that are not just common to humans but also have an ancient lineage, as explained in the next section.

1.3.2 Evolutionary layers of the brain

A well-known model for understanding the basic structure of the human brain was developed by Paul MacLean in the 1960s (see MacLean, 1990). He called it the triune brain and suggested that three distinct brains emerged successively in the course of evolution and now coexist in the human skull. (It was mentioned earlier that evolution could not start building a structure from scratch – this is a good example!)

The 'three brains' in the model proposed by MacLean (Figure 1.4) were:

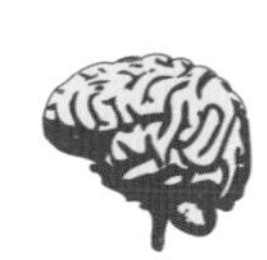

1 The so-called reptilian brain, the oldest of the three in evolutionary terms, which controls the body's vital functions such as heart rate, breathing, body temperature and balance. The main structures here are the brainstem and the cerebellum. One characterisation of the reptilian brain calls it 'reliable but somewhat rigid and compulsive'.
2 The limbic brain. This is also an evolutionarily ancient part of the brain and is found in mammals (such as rats, cats, dogs, monkeys, etc.). In MacLean's schema it includes the amygdala, which registers unconscious memories of behaviours that produced pleasant or frightening experiences,

and is closely linked to emotions, along with the thalamus, hypothalamus and hippocampus. The limbic brain has been characterised as 'the seat of the value judgments that we make, often unconsciously, that exert such a strong influence on our behaviour'.

3 The neocortex (the 'new cortex') evolved more recently in primates such as monkeys and apes, our closest relatives. It constitutes most of the cerebral cortex, which is highly developed in us, with two large cerebral hemispheres. You have already met the prefrontal cortex (PFC), which is part of the neocortex, in Book 1, Section 2.2.2. The neocortex is thought to underlie language, abstract thought, imagination, consciousness and the development of culture and has been characterised as 'flexible, with almost infinite learning abilities'.

Some neuroscientists find the 'triune' brain model simplistic and misleading. Certainly, it should not be taken literally. For instance, the 'reptilian' brain is not a distinct entity, identical to that of reptiles, within our brain. And our so-called 'three brains' do not operate independently of one another – we have one, highly interconnected brain, with different areas communicating with and influencing one another continually.

However, the triune brain concept is helpful in understanding that the influence is not always fully reciprocal – 'older' parts of the brain such as the limbic brain appear to have a stronger influence on the 'newer' parts than vice versa. For instance, neural pathways sending messages from the amygdala to the prefrontal cortex are extensive, but pathways sending messages in the opposite direction are relatively sparse:

As you will see in Chapter 2, this has significance for the conscious control we can exert over our emotions.

The amygdala and emotion

The amygdala, a structure in the limbic brain (Figure 1.4), plays a central role in our emotional perception and responses (LeDoux, 1998). The amygdala has a similar role in other mammals such as rats and monkeys – this is important and relevant, given the use of animal models to study several aspects of issues related to emotions and emotional disorders, as will become clearer in Chapter 2.

Parts of the amygdala are involved in triggering the responses we associate with fear, such as submission, fleeing, or staying rooted to the spot (i.e. freezing). Other regions elicit feelings of 'bliss' or peacefulness, whereas still others evoke aggression and attack.

Life-or-death situations demand extremely rapid responses, which the amygdala is well placed to mediate. For instance, if you are out walking at night in an unfamiliar neighbourhood and hear a sudden thump behind you, it may make you jump in alarm. Your heart will be beating hard and all your senses alert – because the 'fight or flight' reaction that you met in Book 1, Section 2.5.3, has been triggered. Information from the senses (from hearing,

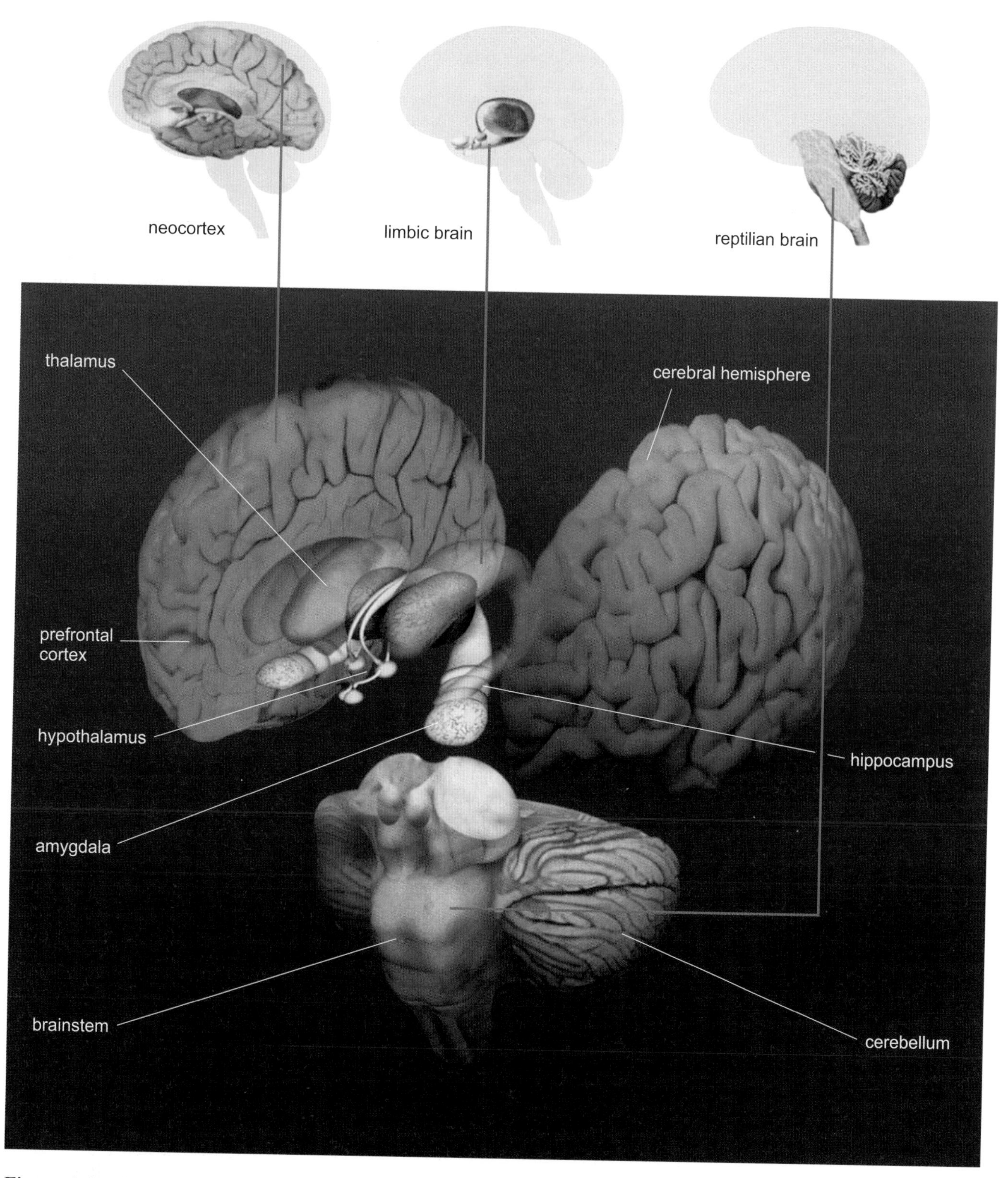

Figure 1.4 The triune brain, showing the so-called reptilian brain, the limbic brain and the neocortex.

in this case) reaches the amygdala, which triggers the 'fight or flight' stress response. There are two routes via which this sensory information can get to the amygdala (Figure 1.5).

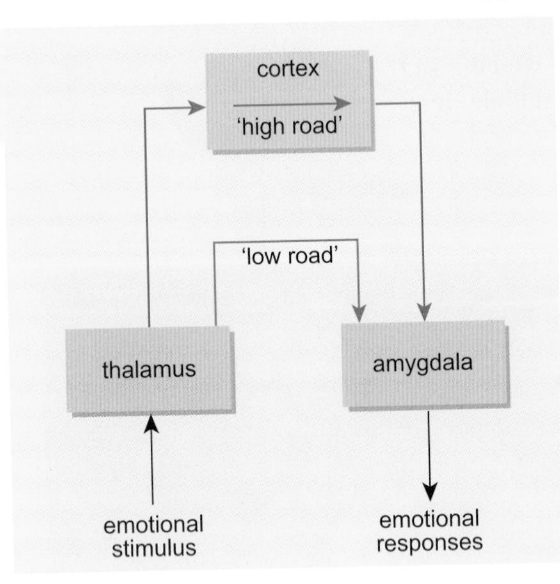

Figure 1.5 Information about emotional stimuli reaches the amygdala via a direct pathway from the thalamus ('low road') as well as by a pathway from the thalamus via the cortex ('high road').

One route, known as the 'low road' or the 'quick and dirty' route, carries relatively crude information from the ear to the amygdala via the thalamus: ear → thalamus → amygdala. This is the **subcortical route** – it is 'below the cortex' and is fast and unconscious – a response is triggered in a split second, before you are aware of what actually made you jump. The other route, the 'high road' is a **cortical route**, as it goes via the cortex: ear → thalamus → cortex → amygdala. It is longer, slower and indirect, but provides more detailed information about the stimulus, and allows conscious awareness and assessment of it. So you may feel rather sheepish on realising that it was just a cat jumping onto a dustbin!

The quick unconscious route elicits an 'automatic' reaction around a fiftieth of a second (20 milliseconds or thousandths of a second) after the sound enters your ear. The longer, slower route via the cortex takes 200 milliseconds (a fifth of a second) – this is how long it takes before you are consciously aware of what made you jump. This is still very quick, but the unconscious route is ten times faster.

The above also shows that our emotions can be triggered extraordinarily rapidly and unconsciously. If we are in a very 'reactive' state, we may find ourselves responding emotionally to situations and stimuli without thought or judgement, perhaps with disastrous results. Fortunately such initial and unconsciously triggered emotional responses can be modified and corrected by conscious appraisals into more considered and appropriate responses. For instance, if someone knocks into you, your response will depend on whether you think the person did this deliberately or accidentally.

We will revisit the role of appraisal, and of the amygdala in emotional responses, in Chapter 2.

1.3.3 The value of negative and positive moods and emotions

An evolutionary stance allows us to be open to the idea that negative as well as positive emotions have value. This is obvious for some negative emotions such as fear and anxiety; for example, in the context of escaping from a bear. It is not so obvious for sadness, or worry (a form of fear and anxiety about the future).

It has been suggested that sadness can be useful in some circumstances and can hence have an 'adaptive' function. For example, it might make individuals reconsider problems such as failed goals, and lead them to abandon unhelpful ways of behaving or of doing things (e.g. Oatley and Johnson-Laird, 1987). To use a physical analogy, pain is unpleasant and aversive but is considered adaptive as it can benefit an injured individual by preventing further harm or damage.

That low mood can indeed be useful is shown in a series of studies carried out by the psychologist Joseph Forgas and his team at the University of New South Wales. They found that, while performing a task, people in whom a sad mood had been induced paid more attention to details, were less gullible, less likely to make errors of judgment, and were more likely to come up with high-quality, persuasive arguments than people in whom a good mood had been induced (Forgas, 2009; mood induction is also considered in Box 4.4).

Good or bad mood can be induced in people by, for instance, showing them happy or sad images or films.

Worry, too, can be useful. Psychologist Graham Davey of the University of Sussex found that although worrying sometimes made things worse for participants in his study, it often motivated them to take action and resolve problems and this in turn reduced anxiety (Davey, 1994). Similarly, McCaul et al. (2007) found that cigarette smokers were more inclined to stop smoking if worried about the risks of smoking. Overall, such findings suggest that mild to moderate levels of worry can be beneficial, motivating people to put in the bit of extra effort and attention needed to make a success of their endeavours.

Conversely, an evolutionary stance allows for the possibility that emotions we consider desirable may not be universally (i.e. in all circumstances) 'good' or appropriate. While there is evidence that positive mood facilitates creativity, flexibility and cooperation (positive emotions are considered in Book 1, Section 3.5 and in Chapter 4 of this book), there is also evidence that misplaced optimism can lead to rash decisions and risk-taking (Alloy and Abramson, 1979).

Aversion and approach are facilitated by different emotions. Low and high mood may be useful in certain situations but may be very unhelpful in others.

1.3.4 The pressures of modern life

A number of studies (for instance, in countries such as the USA) suggest that people currently feel more anxious and stressed than in the 1950s, despite unprecedented improvements in physical health and wealth (e.g. Twenge, 2006). Perhaps this reflects increasing dissatisfaction with the pressures of modern industrial societies, in which the pace of change has been accelerating for many decades.

Figure 1.6 Hunter–gatherers today: A group of Khoisan people of the Kalahari desert singing and dancing around their campfire.

Some researchers suggest that modern life itself is particularly stressful and happiness particularly elusive, because we live in a very different world from that in which we evolved. Culturally, humans have come a long way from their ancestors. Only 30–50 000 years ago our ancestors lived in small kin-groups as hunter–gatherers (Figure 1.6).

This timespan of a few tens of thousands of years, though it may appear long, is not in fact sufficient to allow significant *biological* evolution, though it has witnessed a tremendous explosion of *cultural* evolution. Our brains and emotional propensities, on this account, remain more or less as they were in our ancestors. In Eaton et al.'s

(1988) memorable phrase, modern people are like 'stone-agers in the fast lane'.

What are the implications of this for our well-being? Physically, it has been suggested that many of our chronic health problems, for example atherosclerosis (hardening of the arteries), diabetes, high blood pressure and the complications of smoking and alcohol abuse, result from the mismatch between the environment in which we evolved (sometimes referred to as the **environment of evolutionary adaptation** or **EEA**) and the environment in which we currently live. For instance, we have an evolved propensity to prefer sweet and fatty foods – this would have been valuable for survival in the past, when these energy-rich foods were rare. Now, in an environment of easy availability and little energy expenditure, indulging this preference can lead to obesity and diabetes, with their often harmful consequences.

Mentally and emotionally, too, many people, particularly in urban areas and the industrialised world, now live in a hugely different environment. For instance, many of the expectations that people face from their families, employers and society, and the perceived pressures from advertising and media to achieve goals of fame, beauty and success are unrealistic and unachievable for most people. This can be highly stressful and demoralising. On this view, the complexity of modern goals and the difficulty and effort needed to achieve many of them play a very significant role in feeding negative emotions such as anxiety and depression.

Some people have linked such pressures to the consumer and individualist attitudes in modern industrial societies (e.g. Twenge, 2006). Indeed the distinguished stress researcher Robert Sapolsky of Stanford University argues that the 'epidemic' of stress and stress-related mental distress in Western societies, which are hugely rich and privileged compared to the rest of the world, is strongly linked to psychological factors: 'We're ecologically privileged enough that we can invent social and psychological stress' (Sapolsky, 1998).

■ How would you relate such stress and its effects to the biopsychosocial model?

□ Social and cultural pressures have psychological effects (making people feel stressed and making them feel that they are failures unless they achieve what is considered desirable); psychological stress can trigger the stress system ('fight or flight') and increase the level of hormones such as cortisol (Book 1, Section 3.2.1).

As we will consider in Chapter 2, the effect of chronic stress can be very deleterious for some people.

1.3.5 Social competition, stress and subordination

The behavioural tendencies of animals in situations of defeat and outranking, and hierarchies, have inspired insights into human mental health and well-being.

Living in a group entails competing with others for desirable resources such as food and mates. In many species such competition has led to the development of status hierarchies. Anyone who keeps chickens is well aware that there is a strongly enforced 'pecking order' amongst the hens. This was one of the first dominance hierarchies amongst animals to be described by scientists, and the term 'pecking order' was coined in this context.

Animals who accept subordination avoid fights with dominants; indeed they show clear signals of submission and readily cede space and resources to dominants. They may suffer harassment, displacement and bullying or scape-goating attacks from others (Figure 1.7, Figure 1.8).

(a)

(b)

(c)

(d)

Figure 1.7 Rhesus macaques: the infant son of a subordinate female (who is out of the frame) has been kidnapped and is being mistreated by a dominant female. The infant was distressed and his mother agitated but unable to intervene to rescue him. After some hours, the subordinate female managed to snatch her baby back when the dominant female let go of him.

Why do animals accept subordination in a hierarchy? The simple answer is that strongly social animals normally have no choice. They may be beaten in a fight by a stronger animal or an alliance of animals. But they may be better off remaining in the group because life alone, outside the group, may be even more stressful and dangerous than life as a subordinate. Being in such situations can be very stressful for animals, affecting the levels of stress hormones in their blood, their reproductive systems and their cardiovascular health (Sapolsky, 1998).

Figure 1.8 A young male rhesus macaque wounded in a fight with other males showing submissive posture and fear grimace.

Animals that have been beaten and outranked typically give up – they readily respond in a submissive way to dominant animals, rather than fighting back. This appears to be an evolved, adaptive strategy to being defeated (in situations where rebellion is most unlikely to succeed): it is better to cut one's losses and accept the status quo than to continue fighting and risk injury or even death.

How is this relevant to human mental health? First, status hierarchies are deeply ingrained amongst humans, and social and economic hierarchies and inequalities within and between societies have powerful consequences for poverty, self-esteem and health, including mental health (Book 1, Section 1.2.5; Wilkinson and Pickett, 2009).

Second, humans appear highly sensitive to situations that parallel, or are analogous to, outranking and defeat in animals such as monkeys. The clinical psychologist Paul Gilbert (Gilbert 1989, 1992), building on the suggestions of Price and Sloman (1987), suggests that 'evolutionary-based "social mentalities" that involve ranking and power are activated in depression'. Essentially he believes that depression is a state like that of an outranked, defeated monkey, and is likely to be provoked by situations of loss where a person feels 'helpless and powerless, seeing no way forward'. Gilbert suggests these are also situations in which people are likely to feel humiliated and ashamed.

In support of these suggestions, there is evidence that the situations people find most stressful are 'social evaluation' situations, where not only might they fail, but also they will be *seen* to fail – that is, situations where public humiliation is a possibility. For instance, Dickerson and Kemeny (2004) reviewed studies of cortisol levels in people placed under different kinds of stress. They found that people's cortisol levels were highest in situations where their performance was likely to be assessed in public and where they felt they had no control over their performance (Figure 1.9). (See Box 1.3 for an explanation of the type of data shown in Figure 1.9.)

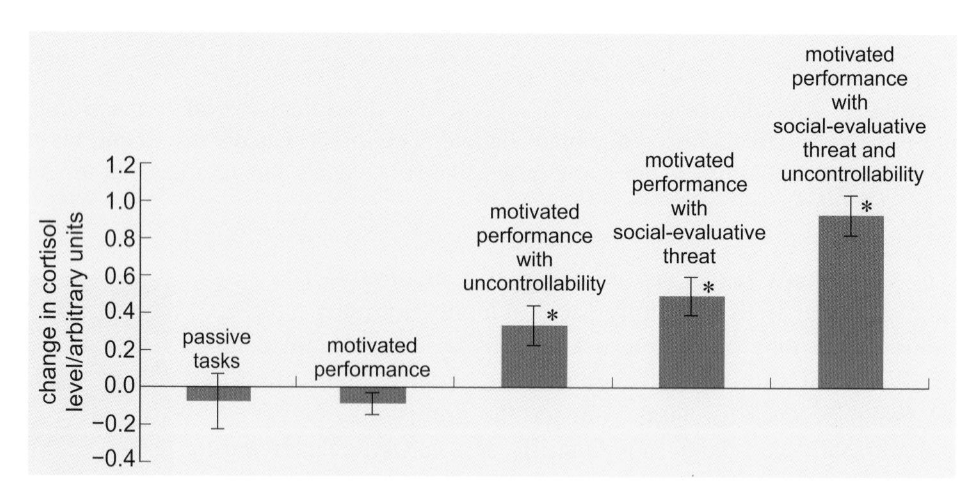

Figure 1.9 Mean (±SEM) change in cortisol levels in potentially stressful situations. Values above 0.0 indicate a rise in cortisol levels. * denotes that the change is statistically significant. Key to terms: *Passive tasks* – tasks such as watching a film that do not require cognitive responses; *Motivated performance* – tasks such as delivering a speech or solving an arithmetical problem that require cognitive responses and achievement of a goal; *Uncontrollability* – a situation of 'forced failure' where participants have no chance of succeeding despite their best efforts, for example where too little time is given to complete a task; *social-evaluative threat* – occurs when an aspect of self (such as ability) could be negatively judged by others.

Some of the changes in cortisol levels shown in Figure 1.9 were **statistically significant**. Statistical significance means that a mathematical test has been applied to the results and has shown there to be a difference that is 'real'; in other words, a difference that is most unlikely to have occurred by chance. When scientists report that the results are *significant*, they mean that they are statistically significant.

You will learn more about how statistical significance is quantified in Book 4, Box 4.1.

Gilbert (1989) suggested that what would be most likely to lead to depression would be:

- situations of direct attack on a person's self-esteem that forced the person into a subordinate position
- events undermining a person's sense of rank, attractiveness and value, particularly via the consequences of the event for roles (for instance, as a mother or professional) that the person held dear; and
- blocked escape.

Testing these ideas, Brown et al. (1995) found that humiliation and entrapment were indeed the most powerful provoking events for the onset of major depression in their study population of women (Table 1.1; see also Box 1.4 for definitions of humiliation, etc.).

Table 1.1 Onsets of major depression by type of provoking event within the six months before onset of depression. (Modified from data in Brown et al., 1995.)

Psychosocial aspects of life event	Number of events that occurred in this category	Number (and %) of events in this category that provoked onset of major depression
Humiliation and entrapment	131	41 (31%)
Loss alone	157	14 (9%)
Danger	89	3 (3%)
Total	377	58 (15%)

The differences shown Table 1.1 are highly statistically significant.

■ From Table 1.1, what is the second most powerful kind of provoking event for the onset of depression?

□ Loss alone – 9% of such events led to depression.

Box 1.3 Research Methods: Analysis of data – descriptive statistics

The data in Figure 1.9 are shown as the mean change in the concentration of cortisol in the blood, plus the SEM (**standard error of the mean**, which is generally written as ±SEM) You will probably be familiar with the term 'mean' which is calculated by adding up all of the data from a group of participants and dividing the total by the number of participants. The mean is sometimes referred to as the average and it allows simple comparisons to be made from one group to another. For example, you can easily see that the mean results for those in a situation of 'motivated performance with social-evaluative threat and uncontrollability' are very different from the results for those in a situation of 'motivated performance with uncontrollability'. However, the mean is a summary of the data obtained and can mask considerable variation within the data. The size of the mean does not tell you anything about the range of the data, in other words the lowest and the highest values. It is possible that some of the values obtained in the first group above were the same as values obtained in the second group above. The second problem with the mean is that it can be distorted by one value that is much higher or lower than the rest of the values obtained for the group. For these reasons, sometimes different ways of summarising data are used, which give a different picture of the data. The first of these is the median, which is found by ranking the data in order of value and taking the middle value (median values are shown in Figure 1.13). The second is the mode, which is the value that occurs most frequently. The mean, median and mode are sometimes referred to as 'measures of central tendency'.

Most scientific data in SDK228, however, is presented in the form of a mean. In order to make sense of differences between means, researchers calculate an additional statistic which takes account of the pattern of the observed values, known as the **variance**. The variance is calculated from the differences between each value and the mean, so the more values there are that are much higher or lower than the mean, the greater the variance will be. The variance is usually quite a large figure relative to the mean value, so the square root of the variance is often used, known as the **standard deviation** (SD). The SD therefore gives an idea of the spread of data about the mean. Alternatively, a further calculation is performed, which takes into account the number of participants, giving an SEM. The SEM gives an idea of the accuracy of the mean, or how close it is to the true population mean. Data is usually presented in the form mean ±SD or mean ±SEM. In graphs, the SD or SEM is usually shown as a small bar (line with a flat top) above and below the mean value, as shown in Figure 1.9.

In summary, descriptive statistics such as the mean, SD and SEM, are used to summarise quantitative data and provide useful information about the values and spread of data obtained in different groups. They allow comparisons between groups. They do not, however, allow any meaning or significance to be inferred from these observations; this requires the application of a relevant statistical test, which is discussed in Book 4, Chapter 4.

Box 1.4 Psychosocial dimensions of life events

(Modified from Kendler et al. (2003).)

- Loss: for example, a real or anticipated loss of a person, a material possession, employment, health, respect in the community or a cherished idea about oneself or someone close to oneself.
- Humiliation: feeling devalued in relation to others or against a core sense of self, usually with an element of rejection or sense of role failure.
- Entrapment: ongoing circumstances of marked difficulty of at least 6 months' duration that the subject can reasonably expect will persist or get worse, with little or no possibility that a resolution can be achieved as a result of anything that might reasonably be done.
- Danger: the level of potential future loss, including both the chance that a given traumatic event will recur or a possible sequence of circumstances in which the full threat or dire outcome has yet to occur.

In Section 1.4 we consider emotional disorders, such as major depression, further.

1.4 Recognising emotional disorders

1.4.1 Experiencing depression

We all have set-backs that can make us feel low, sad or anxious. What is the difference between these states, and states of low mood that are officially considered to be disorders? You might be surprised to learn that in real life there is no clear dividing line to distinguish 'normal' from disordered experience of these emotions, However, we often know when all is not as it should be. First-person accounts, or personal narratives (Sections 1.1 and 1.2, Book 1), like the one given in Vignette 1.1 are illuminating in this regard.

Vignette 1.1 An experience of depression: Lewis Wolpert

Professor Lewis Wolpert (1929–), a distinguished British biologist, generally stable, happily married and with a good job at a university, descended into what was diagnosed as an episode of severe depression. A self-confessed hypochondriac, in the weeks before the episode he had been anxious about the effects of a new drug (flecainide) prescribed by his cardiologist to control his long-standing irregular heartbeat or atrial fibrillation. (The old drug, which he had taken for several years, had become ineffective.) He speculates that this change may have triggered his depression. The new drug gave him morning sickness and severe stomach cramps, which accentuated his hypochondriac streak and made him fear he might have a stroke. Worried, and against his doctor's advice, he cancelled a trip abroad to a science conference. Instead of making him feel better, this made him feel even more distressed and anxious, as he felt he had let down his colleagues. He began having difficulties sleeping and started to think a lot about death. Then one night he had a dream about devils and woke up with a compulsion to kill himself. He writes:

> […] my mental state bore no resemblance to anything I had experienced before. I had had periods of feeling low but they were nothing like my depressed state. I was totally self-involved and negative and thought about suicide all the time. I just wanted to be left alone and remain curled up in my bed all day. I could not ride my bicycle and had panic attacks if left alone too long.
>
> I also had numerous physical symptoms – my whole skin would seem to be on fire and I would on occasion twitch uncontrollably. Each new physical sign caused extreme anxiety. Sleep was very difficult and sleeping pills only seemed to work for a few hours. The future seemed hopeless and I was convinced that I would never recover and would probably end up completely mad.
>
> […] I thought of suicide all the time but did not know how to do it. As I was too scared of heights, jumping from my window which was high up was ruled out […] Nothing gave me pleasure and every decision, no matter how small, increased my anxiety. I had no emotions and was unable to cry but I did retain a macabre sense of humor […] I got a bit better during the day and by evening could read and watch TV, but next morning I was back in the original bad state […] My memory seemed to be failing and I was frightened that I was going insane.
>
> *(Wolpert, 2009, pp.1–2)*

Figure 1.10 Lewis Wolpert (1929–).

Lewis Wolpert (Figure 1.10) found his recovery from the episode was tortuous, involving drugs and psychotherapy (see Chapter 3 for more on his case, and approaches to the treatment of depression). Wolpert was aware that 90% of those who suffer a severe depressive episode have a relapse. Indeed, four years later some of the symptoms of his depression recurred; once again he received treatment and recovered. Since then he has suffered other episodes though none as severe as the first (Wolpert, 2009).

■ Using the accounts of Lewis Wolpert's experience (Vignette 1.1) and of Neha's depression in Book 1, Section 1.1.1 find two similarities and two differences in their experience of depression.

□ *Similarities*: Any two of the following (you may have identified others too): both felt they could identify a trigger to their depressive episode, which appears to have involved a period of significant stress or worry; both experienced unpleasant physical or somatic symptoms; both often thought of death; both felt worse in the morning. *Differences*: Neha readily bursts into tears, whereas Wolpert is unable to cry; there was no specific mention of anxiety in Neha's case, whereas it is prominent in Wolpert's case.

As Wolpert's case shows, depressive episodes do not just include despair, they can also include feelings of panic and anxiety. Indeed feelings of anxiety are almost always present in depression, though anxiety can occur without depression.

1.4.2 Diagnostic criteria for emotional disorders

Formal diagnostic criteria exist to identify emotional disorders. Currently the two most widely used, internationally, are DSM-IV-TR (APA, 2000) or ICD-10 criteria (WHO, 2007)) (see Book 1, Section 4.2.3). Such systems are based on signs and symptoms, which psychologists sometimes group into four categories:

- *mood or emotional symptoms*, for instance feeling sad
- *motivational symptoms*, such as difficulty making decisions
- *cognitive symptoms*, involving thought, such as worry or pessimism, and
- *physical symptoms*, such as bodily aches or pains.

Diagnostic systems such as DSM-IV-TR have been criticised for a number of reasons, some of which will be considered in Section 1.5. However, they have been very influential, so it is important to consider them. They not only determine what diagnosis a patient seeking help receives, but also underpin a great deal of research work into the causes and correlates of mental disorders.

■ Can you suggest how diagnostic criteria might underpin research work?

□ Researchers who are interested in (for instance) whether depression is linked to changes in the brain need to compare the brains of people who are and are not depressed. They often use DSM criteria to decide who is or is not depressed – so these criteria will determine who falls into each of the groups being compared.

Thus the process of diagnosis is clearly critical, as our understanding of emotional disorders is fundamentally underpinned by how we decide who suffers from them.

DSM-IV-TR, which we will focus on here, splits emotional disorders into two clusters, affective disorders and anxiety disorders (Box 1.1).

1.4.3 Affective disorders

Affective or mood disorders include manic-depressive illness or bipolar disorder, which you have already met in Book 1, Section 4.2.2. (It is called bipolar because it has 'two poles': mania and depression). However, by far the most prevalent affective disorder is major depression (MD), which accounts for 80–95% of all depressions. Major depression is sometimes called unipolar disorder to contrast it with bipolar disorder. In MD the individual suffers depressive symptoms (for example, sadness, hopelessness, passivity, sleep and eating disturbances) without ever experiencing mania. In mania, the individual experiences symptoms of extreme elation, expansiveness and irritability, talkativeness, inflated self-esteem, and flight of ideas (see Book 1, Section 4.3.1). DSM-IV-TR distinguishes between two kinds of bipolar disorders, depending on whether the depression has full manic episodes or just 'hypomanic' episodes (episodes that are not as severe as full manic episodes). Table 1.2 lists and provides a brief description of the main affective disorders. Our focus in the rest of this section will be on major depression (MD). Bipolar disorder will not be considered further here as it is extensively covered in Book 1, Section 4.3.1.

Table 1.2 Affective or mood disorders (modified from Bear et al., 2007 adapted from DSM-IV-TR (APA, 2000).)

Name	Description
Major depression (MD), also called major depressive disorder (MDD); unipolar disorder; major depressive episode (MDE); clinical depression	Lowered mood and decreased interest or pleasure in all activities, over a period of at least 2 weeks
Dysthymia or dysthymic disorder	Milder than major depression, but has a chronic, 'smouldering' course, and seldom disappears spontaneously
Bipolar disorder (Type I); was called manic-depressive disorder (see also for mania)	Repeated episodes of mania, or mixed episodes of mania and depression, hence also called manic-depressive disorder. Mania is a distinct period of abnormally and persistently elevated, expansive, or irritable mood and impaired judgement
Bipolar disorder (Type II)	Characterised by hypomania, a milder form of mania that is not associated with marked impairments in judgements or performance, but associated with major depression
Cyclothymia or cyclothymic disorder	Hypomania alternating with periods of depression that are not major, i.e. fewer symptoms and shorter duration
Postnatal depression (PND)	Usually, the depression begins during the first year of parenthood, and ranges in severity from mild to severe
Seasonal affective disorder (SAD)	Depression is more common in the winter months and in the Northern Hemisphere, which suggests to some researchers that brain chemistry is affected by sunlight exposure

Diagnosing major depression (MD)

Between ordinary low mood and serious depression lie a range of depressive experiences of varying degrees of severity – that is, there is a continuum. One important issue for diagnostic schemes is whether to draw a line between 'ordinary sadness' and serious depression and, if so, where this line should be drawn.

DSM-IV-TR (and ICD-10) diagnostic systems are categorical – that is, they are used to decide whether a particular named disorder is *present* or *not present*. In effect, they draw a line through a continuum of experience. It is a bit like deciding that all men over the height of 5 ft 6 in (1.68 m) fall into the category 'tall', while all those under this height fall into the category 'short'.

The DSM-IV-TR criteria for MD are shown in Box 1.5. Depression that does not meet the criteria is categorised as *subclinical depression*, while any depression that does meet the criteria is categorised as *clinical depression*.

As you look at Box 1.5 below, look back also at Lewis Wolpert's account of his depression (Vignette 1.1), and consider how the criteria below relate to his experience.

Box 1.5 Diagnostic criteria for major depressive episode

(Adapted from DSM-IV-TR (APA, 2000).)

The American Psychiatric Association suggests a diagnosis of depression if, during the same 2-week period, a person experiences five (or more) of the following symptoms, which must include either or both of the two primary symptoms:

The primary symptoms are:

1. persistent feelings of sadness or anxiety
2. loss of interest or pleasure in usual activities

The secondary symptoms are:

3. changes in appetite that result in weight losses or gains not related to dieting
4. insomnia or oversleeping
5. loss of energy or increased fatigue
6. restlessness or irritability
7. feelings of worthlessness or inappropriate guilt
8. difficulty thinking, concentrating or making decisions
9. thoughts of death or suicide or attempts at suicide

Note: symptoms should not be counted if:

A They are the direct physiological effects of a substance (drug of abuse, or medication) or a medical condition (e.g. hypothyroidism)

B They would be better accounted for by bereavement (i.e. the loss of a loved one).

- ■ Considering Lewis Wolpert's depressive episode, and the criteria in Box 1.5: (a) Which of the criteria were clearly or probably met in Wolpert's account? (b) Are there any criteria that there might be some uncertainty about? (c) Were there any experiences in Wolpert's account that are not mentioned in the criteria?
- □ (a) All of criteria 1–9 appear to have been met. (b) It is interesting that a change of drug preceded Wolpert's episode; he also had a medical condition (atrial fibrillation). We don't have any information about the extent to which these were responsible for any of the symptoms he experienced – so we don't know if item (A) in the criteria in Box 1.5 applied or not. (c) He mentions physical (somatic) symptoms and deteriorating memory (though the latter could perhaps be covered by criterion 8).

In real life, low mood is a continuum – people can be mildly, moderately or seriously depressed. Scales other than the DSM are used to assess the *level* of depression on a continuum. The Beck Depression Inventory (BDI; Book 1, Box 4.9) is one such scale.

- ■ Can you think of a situation in which it would be useful to have a scale such as the BDI?
- □ In studies where researchers are interested in the efficacy of a particular drug treatment or other intervention, they need to assess the severity of the depression before and after the treatment or intervention. Scoring on a scale such as the BDI would allow such an assessment.

1.4.4 Anxiety disorders

Fear, anxiety and worry are part of normal experience and can all be very useful, as we have seen. However, when they become exaggerated, or attached to inappropriate stimuli or situations, they can interfere with normal functioning and cause immense distress. Anxiety disorders are characterised by constant or intense feelings of apprehension, uncertainty and fear. These feelings are one extreme of a continuum from 'normal' fear to anxiety – the responses differ not in kind but in degree. Both involve the 'fight or flight' system that comes into play in situations of actual or perceived danger (Book 1, Section 2.5.3). Table 1.3 shows a range of anxiety disorders together with brief descriptions of their symptoms.

Table 1.3 Anxiety disorders (from Bear et al., 2007 adapted from DSM-IV-TR (APA, 2000)).

Name	Description
Panic disorder (PD)	Frequent panic attacks consisting of discrete periods with the sudden onset of intense apprehension, fearfulness, or terror, often associated with feelings of impending doom
Agoraphobia	Anxiety about, or the avoidance of, places or situations from which escape might be difficult or embarrassing, or in which help may not be available in the event of a panic attack
Obsessive-compulsive disorder (OCD)	Obsessions, which cause marked anxiety or distress, and/or compulsions, which serve to neutralise anxiety in the short term
Generalised anxiety disorder (GAD)	At least 6 months of persistent and excessive anxiety and worry
Specific phobia	Clinically significant anxiety provoked by exposure to a specific feared object (such as birds or blood) or situation, often leading to avoidance behaviour
Social phobia (or social anxiety)	Clinically significant anxiety provoked by exposure to certain types of social or performance situations, often leading to avoidance behaviour
Post-traumatic stress disorder (PTSD)	The re-experiencing of an extremely traumatic event, accompanied by symptoms of increased arousal and the avoidance of stimuli associated with the trauma

Some anxiety disorders, such as phobias, appear to be provoked by fear of a *specific* danger (Table 1.3). In others, such as GAD, no specific object is known to pose a threat, but strong anxiety is chronic, present almost daily for months on end. In the rest of this section we will focus on GAD.

Experiencing anxiety

GAD is one of the most prevalent emotional disorders (Figure 1.1). It has been estimated that over 5% of people will be diagnosed with GAD in their lifetime, and 12% of those who attend anxiety clinics are diagnosed with GAD (Kessler et al., 2005). Anxiety is also part of mixed anxiety and depression (MAD) one of the most common emotional disorders (Figure 1.1). We will return to MAD in Section 1.5.

The case report in Vignette 1.2 describes one woman's experience of GAD.

Vignette 1.2 Generalised anxiety disorder (GAD) – Suzanna's story

I have been suffering from GAD for nearly 2 years now.

I am no better now than when I was first diagnosed, and I have to say, that I ended up feeling very alone and afraid. [...] I am on disability living allowance due to the severity of my symptoms. I'll list them in the hope that someone else suffering will see them and realise that they are not alone:

- Palpitations
- Chest pain
- Back pain
- IBS [irritable bowel syndrome]
- Stomach pain
- Breathlessness
- Pains in arms and legs
- Constant feeling that I'm going to die
- Insomnia
- Headaches and feelings of tightness in the head
- Blurred vision

There are just too many symptoms to list them all. GAD can manifest itself in so many different physical ways that you end up not knowing what is real and what is part of the anxiety [...] I ended up going to casualty thinking I was having a heart attack, so many times. I [...] continue to believe my symptoms have physical causes. The fact that I'm even writing this shows that somewhere inside, I must be aware that my severe anxiety is causing it. There are just too many symptoms for it to be one physical illness. Doesn't help when you're sat on your own going through it. If I can help anyone, it is by saying that you must be the first person to help yourself. Be stronger than I have managed to be and demand the help you need. This is a real illness and I have been told that it is second only to depression in this country, and yet I cannot find the help I need.

(Anxiety UK, 2007)

Those suffering from GAD (Figure 1.11) are sometimes characterised as 'worriers', with daily life dominated by anxious thoughts. Their muscles may be unusually tense, and they may have hardening of the arteries (Thayer et al., 1996). It appears to be more common amongst poorer people, those with lower education, and those living in urban environments. In the USA it is more common amongst young black people (Blazer et al., 1991), and there is evidence that it is more common in countries in which there is war or political oppression than in countries at peace (Compton et al., 1991).

■ Can you speculate about why GAD might be more common in these situations?

□ These seem to be situations in which people experience a lack of control over their own destinies and future – about violence, their own safety, discrimination and lack of opportunity. These are just the kind of situations where people would be more likely to worry.

Figure 1.11 Chronic worry and anxiety characterise GAD.

Diagnosing generalised anxiety disorder (GAD)

GAD is typically diagnosed if a patient shows anxiety symptoms that do not adequately fit any of the criteria for the other anxiety disorders listed in Table 1.3, but do fulfil those for generalised anxiety disorder. The DSM-IV-TR criteria for GAD are listed in Box 1.6.

As you look at Box 1.6, look back also at Suzanna's account of her anxiety (Vignette 1.2) and think about how her experience relates to the criteria below.

Box 1.6 Brief diagnostic criteria for generalised anxiety disorder

(Adapted from DSM-IV-TR (APA, 2000).)

Criteria A–F need to be satisfied for a diagnosis of GAD.

A – Excessive anxiety and worry (apprehensive expectation), occurring more days than not for at least 6 months, about a number of events or activities (such as work or school performance).

B – The person finds it difficult to control the worry.

C – The anxiety and worry are associated with three (or more) of the following six symptoms, with at least some symptoms present for more days than not for the past 6 months (*Note*: only one item is required in children):

1 restlessness or feeling keyed up or on edge
2 being easily fatigued
3 difficulty concentrating or mind going blank
4 irritability
5 muscle tension
6 sleep disturbance (difficulty falling or staying asleep, or restless unsatisfying sleep).

D – The focus of anxiety and worry is not about having a panic attack (as in panic disorder), being embarrassed in public (as in social phobia), being contaminated (as in obsessive-compulsive disorder), being away from home or close relatives (as in separation anxiety disorder), gaining weight (as in anorexia nervosa), having multiple physical complaints (as in somatisation disorder), or having a serious illness (as in hypochondriasis), and the anxiety and worry do not occur exclusively during post-traumatic stress disorder.

E – The anxiety, worry or physical symptoms cause clinically significant distress or impairment in social, occupational or other important areas of functioning.

F – The disturbance is not due to the direct physiological effects of a substance (e.g. a drug of abuse, a medication) or a general medical condition (e.g. hyperthyroidism) and does not occur exclusively during a mood disorder, a psychotic disorder or a pervasive developmental disorder.

■ Does Suzanna's experience (Vignette 1.2) suggest state or trait anxiety? Explain your answer.

□ Susanna's anxiety is not temporarily elicited by particular circumstances, after which it disappears, as would be the case in state anxiety. Her anxiety seems to be ever-present, so it is like 'trait anxiety' (Box 1.2).

There is evidence that those who have a tendency to be anxious (have trait anxiety) can benefit from psychotherapy, relaxation and meditation (such therapies will be considered in Chapters 3 and 4 of this book).

1.5 Challenges in the diagnosis of depression and anxiety

1.5.1 Detecting depression in primary care settings

People suffering from depression or anxiety often seek informal help at first – consulting friends, neighbours and family, and relevant websites and books. Only if the problem persists are they likely to seek professional help. Typically, the professional consulted will be the family doctor or GP.

People experiencing emotional distress may seek out a GP because they are experiencing physical symptoms such as back pain, heart palpitations, sleeping difficulties, tiredness, loss of appetite, etc. For such symptoms, GPs may need to exclude some conditions, such as hypothyroidism (see Book 1, Section 4.3.4).

GPs often do make independent decisions about whether a patient is suffering from an emotional disorder or not, though if they feel uncertain, or if the disorder seems very serious, the patient may be referred to specialists in mental health diagnosis and care, such as psychiatrists (Book 1, Section 4.1.2).

Ideally, a GP would have the time and resources to carry out appropriate psychological and physiological tests, and to spend time assessing anyone who was suffering from emotional disorder. However, as the average GP visit in the UK lasts only a few minutes, this is a counsel of perfection. Indeed a meta-analysis (see Box 1.7 for what a meta-analysis involves) of studies involving over 50 000 patients concluded that GPs do not recognise depression in a significant number of those who have it, and also frequently diagnose it in people who do not have it (Mitchell et al., 2009).

Box 1.7 Research Methods: Meta-analysis

A **meta-analysis** ('meta' means 'high-level' so meta-analysis means 'high-level analysis') considers the results of previous studies (published, and sometimes unpublished) on a specific topic to reach a more reliable overall conclusion. This is a very valuable process since it allows researchers to make sense of the often conflicting information that is presented by individual studies. In addition, meta-analyses can help in understanding precisely why individual studies show different or conflicting results. For instance, one study may show that Treatment X works, while another study may show that the same treatment doesn't work. A meta-analysis might identify a variable (such as the 'age of participants') that explains the discrepancy: the first study may have been conducted with older people, and the second with younger people. This would suggest the possibility that Treatment X is effective with older patients but not with younger ones.

Meta-analyses need to be done carefully to try to make sure that the measures used in the different studies are comparable. For instance, if an emotional disorder such as major depression is assessed in different ways in some studies than in others, then this could confuse the results of the meta-analysis.

Mitchell et al. (2009) selected studies where GPs were making routine 'unassisted' diagnoses – based on their own judgment, 'without specific help from severity scales, diagnostic instruments, education programmes, or other organisational approaches' – that is, the way GPs normally make diagnoses.

The accuracy of the GPs' diagnoses of depression had been assessed independently in each of the studies included in the meta-analysis, using DSM or ICD criteria for depression. Thus Mitchell and his colleagues had information about the extent to which GPs got the diagnosis of depression right or wrong.

They found that: 'In general, a motivated GP in an urban setting (where the rate of prevalence of depression is 20%) would correctly diagnose 10 out of 20 cases, missing 10 true positives. The GP would correctly reassure 65 out of 80 non-depressed individuals, falsely diagnosing 15 people as depressed'.

- (a) What is the percentage of true cases of depression misdiagnosed? Are these false negatives or false positives?

  (b) What is the percentage of non-depressed people incorrectly diagnosed as depressed? Are these false negatives or false positives?

- (a) 10 out of 20, that is 50%, of people are misdiagnosed as OK, even though they are depressed. These are false negatives (see Book 1, Box 4.7).

  (b) 15 out of 80, that is 18.75%, of people who are not depressed are incorrectly diagnosed as depressed. These are false positives (see Book 1, Box 4.7).

The number of people misdiagnosed as false negatives or false positives (from above, 15 + 10 = 25 out of 100, 1 in 4, or 25%) is therefore substantial. Moreover, as GPs prescribe antidepressant drug treatment and make referrals for counselling and therapy, this means some people who need treatment will not be offered it, while others may be prescribed treatment they do not need.

Where drug treatments are offered to false positives, this can be problematic, as drugs typically have side effects and can be difficult to come off. Fortunately the evidence also suggests that GPs are less likely to misdiagnose serious cases of depression (Mitchell et al., 2009).

The above should not be seen as a criticism of the diagnostic abilities of GPs. As Tyrer (2009) points out, the diagnosis of depression is fraught with difficulty even for experts, so it is not surprising that misdiagnosis, especially of milder and moderate cases of depression, occurs. The fact that depression is often mixed with anxiety, as we consider below, may make diagnosis even trickier.

Activity 1.1 Factors affecting diagnosis of emotional disorders in a primary care setting

(LO 1.3) Allow 20 minutes

Take a few minutes to think about, and make a list of, factors that might help a GP (working in the normal way, without assistance) to assess a patient more accurately for an emotional disorder such as depression. This activity should help you appreciate the factors at play in a primary care setting that may impact on diagnosis, and should feed into your understanding of treatment availability and options (considered in Chapter 3).

Some people complaining of somatic symptoms may not be sensitive to, or may be unwilling to acknowledge, emotional suffering in themselves. Some may feel that somatic symptoms will be taken more seriously by the medical profession, or be more amenable to medical treatment. Hence they may be more likely to mention these to a doctor than feelings of anxiety and depression. Personal and cultural values may come into play here, too – for instance, the evidence suggests that there may be a gender difference, with men less likely to report emotional distress than women.

1.5.2 Are the diagnostic categories correct?

According to DSM-IV-TR, if the criteria for two or more disorders – such as MD and GAD – are each satisfied in the same person, the disorders are comorbid (Book 1, Section 4.3.5).

In fact, MD and GAD are often comorbid. Figure 1.12 shows the odds ratios for having an anxiety disorder at the same time as major depression. Box 1.8 explains what an **odds ratio** is.

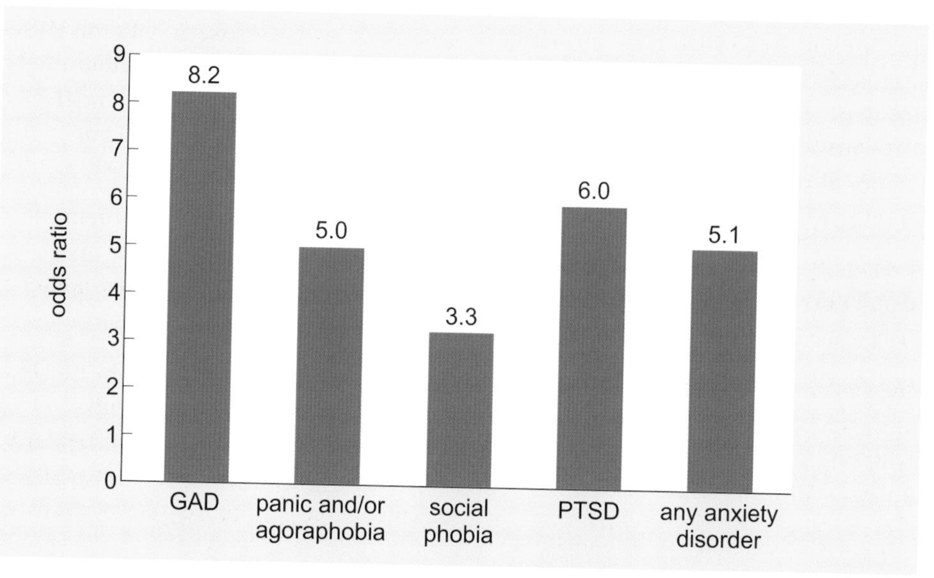

Figure 1.12 Likelihood that a comorbid anxiety disorder is also present in patients diagnosed with major depression (MD).

Box 1.8 Odds ratio

Imagine that the chances in the USA of adult men having GAD are on average 1 in 100. But what of the subset of adult men who already have MD? What are the chances that such men will have GAD as well as MD? An odds ratio tells us about the increase in the chance that such men will have GAD, already having MD. If having MD increases the chances of having GAD from the usual 1 in 100 to 8.2 in 100, then the odds ratio for having GAD when you have MD is 8.2. If having MD has no effect at all on the chances of having GAD, then the odds ratio is 1.00 (it does not affect the odds). An odds ratio of 1.05 means for the population of men with MD the chances of having GAD are increased by 5%. The further away from 1 the odds ratio is, the stronger the effect.

- Speculate about what this kind of pairing between MD and GAD might suggest.

- That there is some connection between the two conditions. For instance: (i) one causes the other; (ii) both are due to a common cause; (iii) there is just one underlying condition with a range of symptoms, with some symptoms matching the (artificially set up) criteria for one condition and others matching the criteria for the other condition.

In practice, it is increasingly recognised that in many cases a person has *some* symptoms of depression (but not enough to justify a diagnosis of depression), and *some* symptoms of anxiety (but not enough to justify a diagnosis of anxiety). Neither DSM-IV-TR nor ICD-10 provide for the proper diagnosis of such a condition. However, an increasing number of researchers recognise this as mixed anxiety and depression disorder (MADD), also called **mixed anxiety and depression** (**MAD** – see Figure 1.1) or cothymia (Tyrer, 2001). Indeed MAD was found to occur in around 55% of all those suffering from an emotional disorder (or common mental disorder) (McManus et al., 2009), making it the most common emotional disorder by far.

The existence of strong comorbidity between anxiety and depression, and mixed anxiety and depressive disorder, have led some researchers to suggest that these disorders lie on an anxiety–depression continuum or spectrum.

Indeed there is evidence to suggest that 'cases' of disorder might map onto a single spectrum of 'counts of mental symptoms', with no evidence for clustering of symptoms into disorders such as those proposed by DSM-IV-TR and ICD-10 (Das-Munshi et al., 2008; Melzer et al., 2002).

Using a CIS-R scale (Clinical Interview Schedule – Revised scale – see Box 1.9), Das-Munshi et al. (2008) assessed the presence of symptoms of mental disorder and mapped them onto 'recognised' depression and anxiety disorders such as MD, GAD, MAD and comorbid anxiety and depression.

Box 1.9 Clinical Interview Schedule – Revised (CIS-R)

The CIS-R is a structured interview schedule used in national surveys such as the *Adult Psychiatric Morbidity in England, 2007: results of a household survey* (McManus et al., 2009) to assess neurotic symptoms and common mental disorders in the population. (Clinical interviews are described in Book 1, Section 4.3.2.) For each interviewee, the severity of symptoms such as fatigue, concentration and forgetfulness, sleep problems, irritability, depressive ideas, depression, anxiety, panic, worry about physical health, compulsions, obsessions and so on, is scored on a scale of 0–4 (0–5 in the case of depressive ideas). The scores are summed to give an overall severity score: a score of 12 or more indicates a significant level of symptoms, and a score of 18 or more suggests treatment is needed. In the APMS (2007) interviewees' answers to the CIS-R were also used to derive ICD-10 diagnoses of GAD, MD, phobias, OCD and panic disorder. MAD was defined as having a CIS-R score of 12 or more but falling short of the criteria for any other common mental disorder.

The distribution of CIS-R scores they obtained for the four different disorders (and for 'no diagnosis') is shown in Figure 1.13.

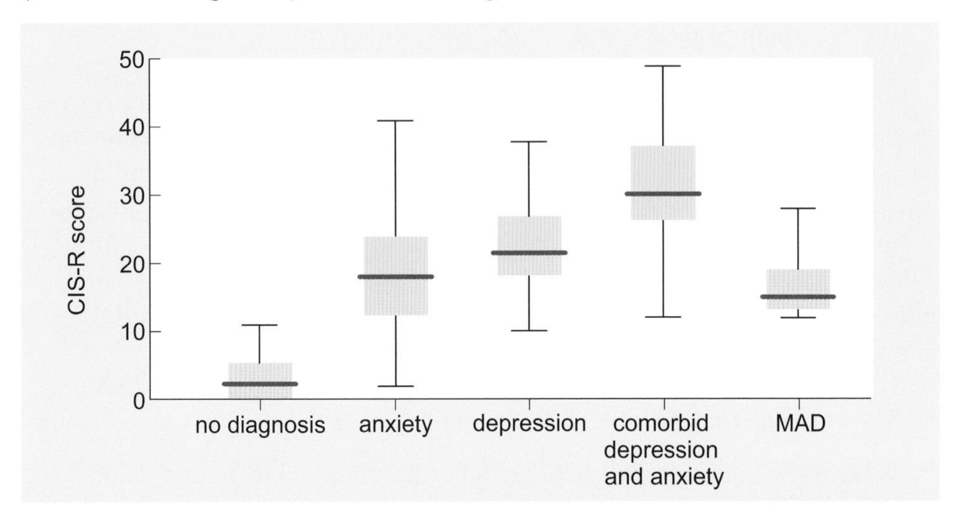

Figure 1.13 Box plot distributions of CIS-R symptom scores for five diagnostic groups. In a box plot distribution, 50% of the scores obtained (between 25% and 75%) lie inside the box. The horizontal line across each box shows the median score (see Box 1.3). The bars above and below the box show the range of scores in each case, from minimum (at bottom of bar) to maximum (at top of bar).

■ The higher the CIS-R score, the more serious on average a disorder is likely to be. On this basis, looking at Figure 1.13, which of the four disorders would appear to be least serious and which would appear to be most serious?

□ Mixed anxiety-depression would be least serious; comorbid depression and anxiety would be most serious.

Interestingly, such critiques appear to be having some impact. The next version of the DSM (DSM-V, expected 2013), while still applying a categorical approach, proposes a new disorder called mixed anxiety-depression.

1.5.3 Medicalising sadness?

Depressive disorders are amongst the most commonly diagnosed mood disorders. Indeed by some accounts there is a veritable epidemic of depression all across the world (Murray and Lopez, 1996).

Some critics have suggested that the apparent increase in depressive disorders may be due to changes in the criteria used to diagnose depression. The main issue here is how to distinguish depressive disorder from normal suffering. DSM's own definition of a mental disorder is that a disorder involves a dysfunction *in an individual*; hence an *expected response* to a stressor should not be considered a disorder. Critics argue that DSM's own criteria subvert this definition – DSM lists the symptoms that must be present for a given diagnosis, but ignores the *context* in which the symptoms developed.

- ■ Why might context be important here?
- □ In some contexts the kinds of symptoms listed for a diagnosis of depressive disorder might be a normal and expected response to a stressor; in other words, the suffering is 'normal', not 'dysfunctional'.

DSM-IV-TR is thus accused of medicalising ordinary, in the sense of 'to be expected in the circumstances', sadness; that is, of having criteria that allow conflation of the kind of sadness expected after a loss or disappointment, with the altogether different phenomenon of long-term and apparently inexplicable 'melancholia' (Horwitz and Wakefield, 2007). For example, DSM-IV-TR, while recognising the legitimacy of depressive symptoms for 2 months following bereavement in the shape of the loss of a loved one, does not recognise that other losses (e.g. of a job, a marriage) can also be a form of bereavement and lead to depressive symptoms.

- ■ What is the effect of DSM-IV-TR ignoring other contexts that could legitimately precipitate a loss or bereavement response?
- □ Depressive disorder (rather than context-related sadness or grief) would be diagnosed. This could lead to inflation of the number of cases of depressive disorder diagnosed and referred for treatment.

Ordinary sadness is a common human experience that may have an adaptive function (Section 1.3.3), and for most people it dissipates on its own without treatment in days or weeks. Nevertheless, it is probably the case that many people experiencing it find it unacceptable and unbearable, and welcome any diagnosis that allows treatment and relief from the symptoms.

Indeed many people now appear to see low mood and anxiety as a 'disease' that can and should be cured as quickly as possible with drugs. Thus some of those who experienced low mood and anxiety as a consequence of severe financial set-backs or job losses in the UK recession of 2009 apparently 'pressured' their doctors into prescribing antidepressant and other pills, wanting a 'quick fix', even though other forms of help (such as advice on how to cope with debt) might have been more appropriate.

1.6 Final word

While acknowledging the biological antecedents and value of emotions such as sadness and anxiety, and the possibility that 'ordinary' sadness and anxiety may now be over-diagnosed as disorders and over-medicalised, we must not forget that we are dealing with a spectrum of severity. Thus, far from being ordinary, major depression is an *extreme form* of sadness – described by those like Lewis Wolpert who have experienced it (Vignette 1.1) as 'malignant sadness' (Wolpert, 2001). There can be no doubt that severe depression is a disorder, associated as it is with self-harm, inability to work and even suicide.

What might underlie such disorders, and why do some people experience such extremes of sadness, and of other emotions such as anxiety, while others do not? This is a question that will be addressed in Chapter 2, where we consider the possible causes of emotional disorders.

1.7 Summary of Chapter 1

- Any examination of emotional disorders needs to be done against the backdrop that emotional phenomena have evolved over millions of years, and that negative as well as positive emotions have functions. There is evidence that sadness and worry can be beneficial.
- The concept of the 'triune brain' postulates that the human brain can be thought of as 'three brains'. Some are 'ancient' in evolutionary terms, while others are newer. Parts of our brains are very similar to those in other animals, and include the brain bases of emotional responses such as the fear response.
- There is good evidence for the universality of emotions such as fear, anger, sadness and joy amongst humans, as a result of shared biological bases. However, culture affects which emotions are displayed and what they are associated with.
- Observations of the behavioural tendencies of animals in situations of defeat and outranking have inspired important insights into human depression and anxiety.
- DSM-IV-TR distinguishes between affective (or mood) disorders and anxiety disorders. First-person experiences of major depression (MD) and generalised anxiety disorder (GAD) are described and considered in the light of DSM criteria for these disorders.
- There are established diagnostic criteria for deciding whether particular affective or anxiety disorders are present in an individual or not. However, the process of diagnosing such disorders is not straightforward. This is an important issue, not just for the treatment of patients suffering from emotional disorders (for instance, GPs get a significant proportion of diagnoses of major depression wrong) but also for those trying to clarify the risk factors for these disorders.

1.8 Learning outcomes

LO 1.1 Recognise the value of an evolutionary perspective in understanding the function of emotions (or moods) and the roots of emotional (or mood) disorders. (KU1, KU3, CS1, CS2)

LO 1.2 Specify brain pathways and structures involved in the perception and processing of emotions and emotional reactions. (KU1, KU3, CS1, CS2)

LO 1.3 Describe the rationale and limitations of approaches used in the diagnosis of emotional (or mood) disorders, and demonstrate understanding of the factors that influence diagnosis. (KU1, CS1, CS4)

LO 1.4 Outline the characteristics and experience of, and demonstrate understanding of the symptoms and diagnosis of, specified emotional disorders. (KU1, CS1, CS4)

LO 1.5 Demonstrate understanding of, and be able to interpret, information about the prevalence of mental health disorders in populations. (KU1, KU5, CS1, CS2, CS3)

LO 1.6 Demonstrate understanding of the biopsychosocial model in the context of emotions and emotional disorders. (KU1, KU3, CS1, CS2)

1.9 Self-assessment questions

SAQ 1.1 (LOs 1.1 and 1.2)

Following a sudden sound, which of the following pathways, A to E, provides (a) the unconscious route that mediates the fear reaction; (b) the conscious route that mediates the fear reaction and also allows appraisal of the stimulus that caused the fear?

A ear → amygdala → cortex → hippocampus → emotional response

B ear → orbitofrontal cortex → thalamus → emotional response

C ear → thalamus → amygdala → emotional response

D ear → thalamus → cortex → emotional response

E ear → thalamus → cortex → amygdala → emotional response.

SAQ 1.2 (LO 1.3)

Jean has lost her beloved husband and consequently has been feeling very low for the past two weeks. Bill has lost his job and is feeling similarly low. Symptoms 1, 2, 3, 4, 5, and 8 in Box 1.4 definitely apply to both Jean and Bill. Are they equally likely to be diagnosed as suffering major depression (MD)? Explain your answer.

SAQ 1.3 (LO 1.4)

Look at Suzanna's case (Vignette 1.2). Does it satisfy DSM-IV-TR criterion C for the diagnosis of GAD (Box 1.6)? Give reasons for your answer.

SAQ 1.4 (LO 1. 5)

Look at Figure 1.12. What is the odds ratio that 'any anxiety disorder' will be present in people who have major depression? What does this mean?

SAQ 1.5 (LO 1.6)

Which kind of model best fits with Ekman's neurocultural theory of emotions? Give a brief explanation of your answer.

Chapter 2 Towards understanding the aetiology of depression and anxiety

Saroj Datta

2.1 Introduction

Chapter 1 introduced you to the study of emotions and emotional disorders in the context of our evolutionary heritage, and went on to consider how we might recognise emotional disorders, together with some of the problems associated with diagnosis and classification.

In this chapter we move on to consider some risk and causal factors for some depression and anxiety disorders – that is, the possible aetiology of such disorders. A multiplicity of genetic, neurobiological, psychological and social factors are likely to be relevant – this should remind you of the biopsychosocial model of mental health which you met in Book 1. However, it would be impossible to cover even a fraction of them adequately in one chapter so we will focus on a limited number.

You will notice that stress forms the backbone of this chapter. This is no accident, as the role of stress has attracted much attention in the last few decades, and it is now recognised as a powerful factor in the aetiology of emotional disorders. We start by considering what is meant by stress, how it is perceived and the evidence that it is a risk factor for the development of emotional disorders. We then move on to look at the biology of stress, in particular how it affects the brain.

The theme of effects on the brain is continued with a consideration of what has been learnt about the brain mechanisms underlying depression from the workings of antidepressants. Finally, we consider the interaction between genes and the environment, and how this might influence the development of emotional disorders.

2.2 Understanding the role of stress

Look back at some of the cases of depression and anxiety described in Book 1 and Chapter 1 of this book – stressful experiences seem to have been important in triggering or maintaining emotional disorders.

It is often the case that those developing depression or anxiety have experienced significant stress in childhood or in adult life or both. A case of work-related stress that precipitated serious depression is described in Vignette 2.1.

Vignette 2.1 An experience of stress

The following extract is taken from an interview with a 43-year-old woman, who was diagnosed with depression at 40.

Background: Is a divorced part-time carer. Before her depression and suicide attempt she was a workaholic in a job that was becoming more demanding. Her depression required hospitalisation.

'Work had always been really important to me and I'm more like a perfectionist. So everything has to be a 100%, you know, and all that. And I got made promotion several times with my job, and then suddenly, I think like many companies, people started making people redundant, and requesting people to take on more and more and more. In the end I was doing the job 5 people used to do. I was enjoying it. I enjoyed it to the point where it was just getting, physically it was just getting an impossibility. But I'd always loved my job, but it was then becoming that I was away 5, 6 days a week, getting home and I couldn't get away from work basically, because I would get back here and there would be faxes and messages and goodness knows what and … A lot of my job was travelling a lot I was covering a huge area, not just the UK. And one day I just sort of came home after I had been away for a week, parked my car outside, sat on the pavement and just broke down, basically.'

(Health Experience Research Group, 2010)

2.2.1 What do we mean by stress?

We tend to think of 'stress' as a state of demand that is likely to stretch us to breaking point, and hence as a bad thing, to be avoided. An image of stress this brings to mind is pulling on a chain with increasing force: sooner or later the chain will break at the weakest link, leading to collapse. However Hans Selye, the distinguished Austro-Hungarian endocrinologist who developed the concept of stress in the 1930s, felt this was a very one-sided view – he regarded stress as ubiquitous and vitally important, calling it 'the salt of life' (Selye, 1978 [1956]). Selye distinguished two kinds of stress:

The distinction between eustress and distress is not current, but Selye and others found it helpful to understand how stress could be 'good' as well as 'bad'.

> Within the general concept of stress … we must differentiate between *distress* (from the Latin dis = bad, as in dissonance, disagreement), and *eustress* (from the Greek eu = good, as in euphonia, euphoria). During both eustress and distress the body undergoes virtually the same nonspecific responses to the various positive or negative stimuli acting upon it. However, the fact that eustress causes much less damage than distress graphically demonstrates that it is 'how you take it' that determines, ultimately, whether you can adapt successfully to change.
>
> *(Selye, 1978 [1956]), p. 29)*

The critical point that Selye was making is that an understanding of biology by itself may not be enough to understand the effects of stress because the same physiological mechanism underlies both positive and negative stress. Selye's point about 'how you take it' is relevant to the concept of 'appraisal' (Section 2.2.4).

Selye saw a **stressor** as anything eliciting the physiological stress or 'emergency' response (Book 1, Section 3.2.3). The stress response is elicited not just in a classic 'fight or flight' situation, but also when the body is fighting an infection, and in situations that are stimulating and enjoyable, such as 'playing a game of tennis, or engaging in a passionate kiss' (Selye, 1978 [1956]; Figure 2.1). Emotions such as joy, anger and fear are potent elicitors of the stress response. Expectations play a part in generating stress too. Stress is present, for instance, if people believe – correctly or incorrectly – that something threatening or unpleasant is just round the corner. John and Stacey, who have OCD (Book 1, Section 1.1.1 and Case Report 4.3, respectively), suffer from stress generated in this way.

Figure 2.1 Both pleasant (a, b) and unpleasant events or situations (c, d) have the potential to activate the biological stress response.

Despite Selye's broad definition of stress, when used in the context of emotional disorders, the term is generally taken to mean negative stress (or distress). Unfortunately it is virtually impossible to live a life free from this form of stress and whilst it has been suggested that the experience of mild to moderate levels of stress in early life may 'inoculate' animals and people against more serious stress later on (e.g. Maddi, 2006), severe or chronic stress can have very damaging effects, as you will see next.

2.2.2 Recent life events and stress

Many episodes of depression and anxiety are apparently associated with a severe or chronic stressor. Loss of a loved one, unemployment, divorce, poverty, racism and discrimination, illness, a car accident, being mugged, are just some examples. Research supports this notion. For instance, Kenneth Kendler and his team (e.g. Kendler and Prescott, 2006) found that the onset of episodes of major depression (MD) and generalised anxiety disorder (GAD) was strongly linked to stressful life events in the last month in their study population of women (Figure 2.2).

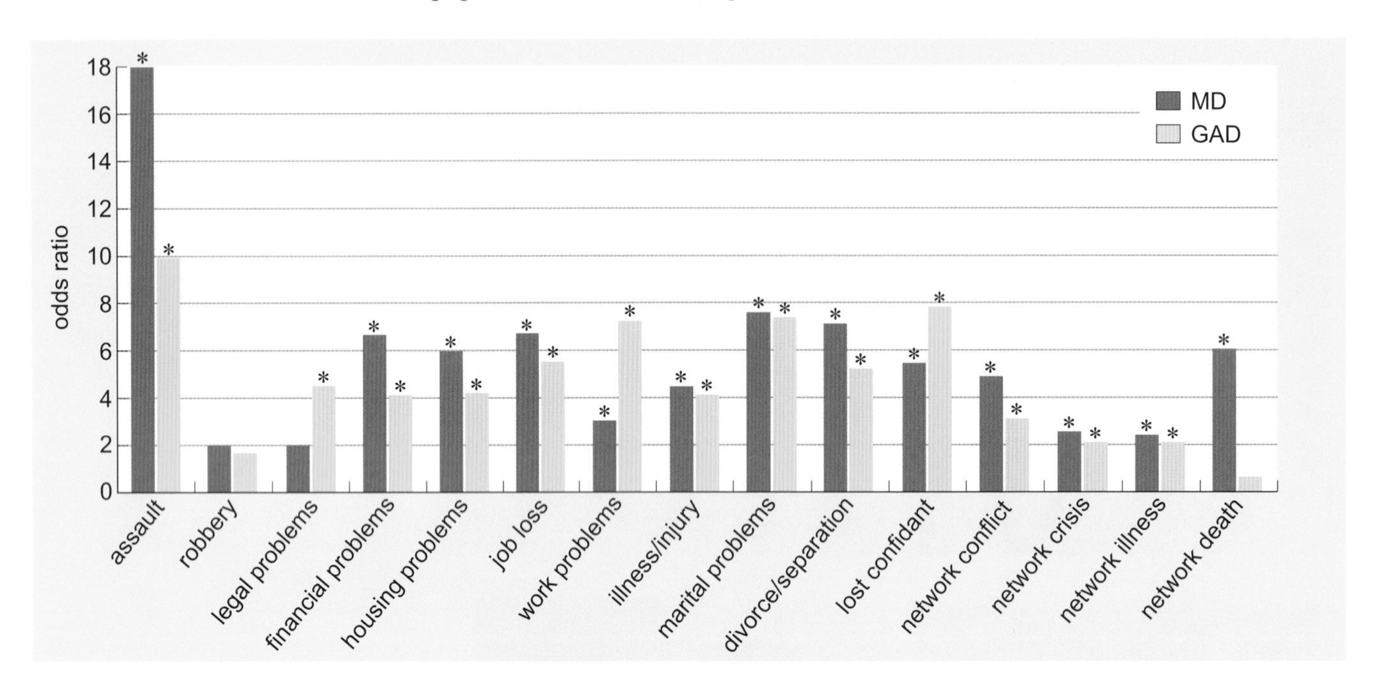

Figure 2.2 Odds ratios for major depression (MD) and generalised anxiety disorder (GAD) among women, associated with the occurrence of a life event in the same month. 'Network' is a woman's social network, such as family and friends. * indicates that the odds ratio for MD or GAD associated with the given life event is statistically significant.

- ■ Using the information in Figure 2.2, which disorder, MD or GAD, do women who have experienced assault tend to develop? Explain your answer.

- □ Odds ratios (see Box 1.8) in Figure 2.2 indicate the increase in the chances of women experiencing MD or GAD following different life events. After assault, the odds ratio for developing MD is 18, while the odds ratio for developing GAD is 10. Thus after an assault women appear more likely to develop MD than GAD.

The chances of experiencing depression and anxiety are increased if a number of stressful life events follow in quick succession (Neha in Book 1 provides a good example), if events are experienced as severe, and if they involve significant loss or personal humiliation (Kendler et al., 2003; Section 1.3.5).

The chances of experiencing such disorders are also increased if other risk factors are present (Turner and Lloyd, 1995). For instance, in January 2010, the Office for National Statistics (ONS) reported that the number of suicides in the UK had risen sharply since the recession began, reversing the downward trend of the previous decade. Suicides rose by 6% from 5377 deaths in 2007 to 5706 deaths in 2008 among people over 15. Commenting on these results, Professor Rory O'Connor of Stirling University's Suicidal Behaviour Research Group said: 'Sadly this increase in suicide is not unexpected given we know there's a relationship between past recessions and an increase in suicides … as well as the financial implications, there's added stress on families and relationships, as well as the loss of social networks to support people' (Bowcott, 2010).

However, the situation is even more complex because some personality traits can kindle stressful situations. Some stressful life events are independent of our own actions, but in others our actions may have helped create the stressful circumstances.

■ Can you think of an example of a stressful life event that is independent of, and one that may be dependent on, our own actions?

□ Natural disasters such as earthquakes and hurricanes would fall into the first category. Many relationship crises may fall into the second.

The chances of experiencing the second kind of stressful life event are higher in those with a 'difficult' or 'neurotic' temperament compared to those with a more 'easygoing' temperament (Section 2.2.5).

2.2.3 Early life events and stress

One of the most potent factors associated with mental disorders such as depression and anxiety later in life is mistreatment and abuse in childhood (Browne and Finkelhor, 1986; Turner and Lloyd, 1995). This includes sexual abuse as well as physical, mental and emotional neglect or mistreatment.

Child sexual abuse affects at least twice as many females as males and appears to be a particularly powerful risk factor for adult-onset depression (Weiss et al., 1999). It is also a strong predictor of post-traumatic stress disorder (Browne and Finkelhor, 1986). It may therefore be a factor that contributes to the well-established epidemiological finding that women are much more likely to be diagnosed with depression and other emotional disorders than men, not only in England (Figure 1.1) but around the world (Weissman et al., 1996).

Childhood abuse may have psychosocial consequences that increase the risk of depression, as it can lead to shame, humiliation, isolation and an inability to trust others.

Another possibility is that, especially if severe and repeated, childhood abuse biologically sensitises the stress response systems of children so that stress is triggered much more easily later on, and for longer periods (Perry et al, 1995).

An important study by Christine Heim and her associates (Heim et al., 2000) showed that the stress response of women who had suffered childhood abuse (sexual or physical) did indeed show evidence of having been 'sensitised'. The women in Heim's study fell into four groups:

1 ELS/MD: those who experienced early life stress (ELS) – that is, were sexually or physically abused as children, and were also diagnosed with major depression (MD) in adulthood

2 ELS/no MD: those who were abused in childhood but did not get major depression
3 No ELS/MD: those who did not suffer child abuse but had major depression
4 Controls: those with no history of childhood abuse or major depression, who acted as a control group.

All the women underwent the Trier social stress test, which involves public speaking and solving arithmetical problems in front of a critical audience. The levels of the stress hormones ACTH (adrenocorticotropic hormone) and cortisol (you met these hormones in Book 1, Section 3.2.2) in the women's blood were measured before, during and after the test, as were their heart rates (Figure 2.3). You may recall from Book 1 that when individuals feel threatened the SNS (sympathetic nervous system) is activated and this leads to the release of adrenalin, which elevates heart rate. Stressors also trigger a parallel stress response involving the hypothalamus, which triggers release of ACTH from the pituitary gland, which in turn triggers the release of cortisol from the adrenal cortex (Book 1, Section 3.2.2).

Figure 2.3 shows that before the Trier test, the four groups of women did not differ significantly on any of the three measures of stress, but some clear differences emerged during the test.

■ Look at Figure 2.3a. Was there a clear difference in the ACTH response between women who had and had not experienced childhood abuse?

□ Yes, Figure 2.3a shows several points at which ACTH levels were significantly higher in women who had been abused as children (ELS/MD or ELS/no-MD) than in women who had not been abused (no-ELS/MD or controls).

Women whose stress systems were most reactive in the test were those who had been abused in childhood and were also currently depressed (ELS/MD). They showed the most extreme responses in all three measures – a rise in levels of ACTH and cortisol and an increased heart rate. Thus there is evidence for a marked sensitisation of the stress response system, and a link with depression, in at least some women who experience childhood abuse.

However, note that not all women who experience childhood abuse develop depression (ELS/no-MD group), and not all women who are depressed as adults have experienced childhood abuse (the no-ELS/MD group). This suggests that other risk factors must be operating for depression to develop. There are many possibilities. For those who were abused, the level and kind of abuse may matter. Social and psychological support networks available during childhood and adulthood, or genes that make some women more vulnerable to stress or affect other personality factors, could also play a part.

Having considered the role of stressful life experiences we next look at how cognitive factors can also play a part in emotional disorders.

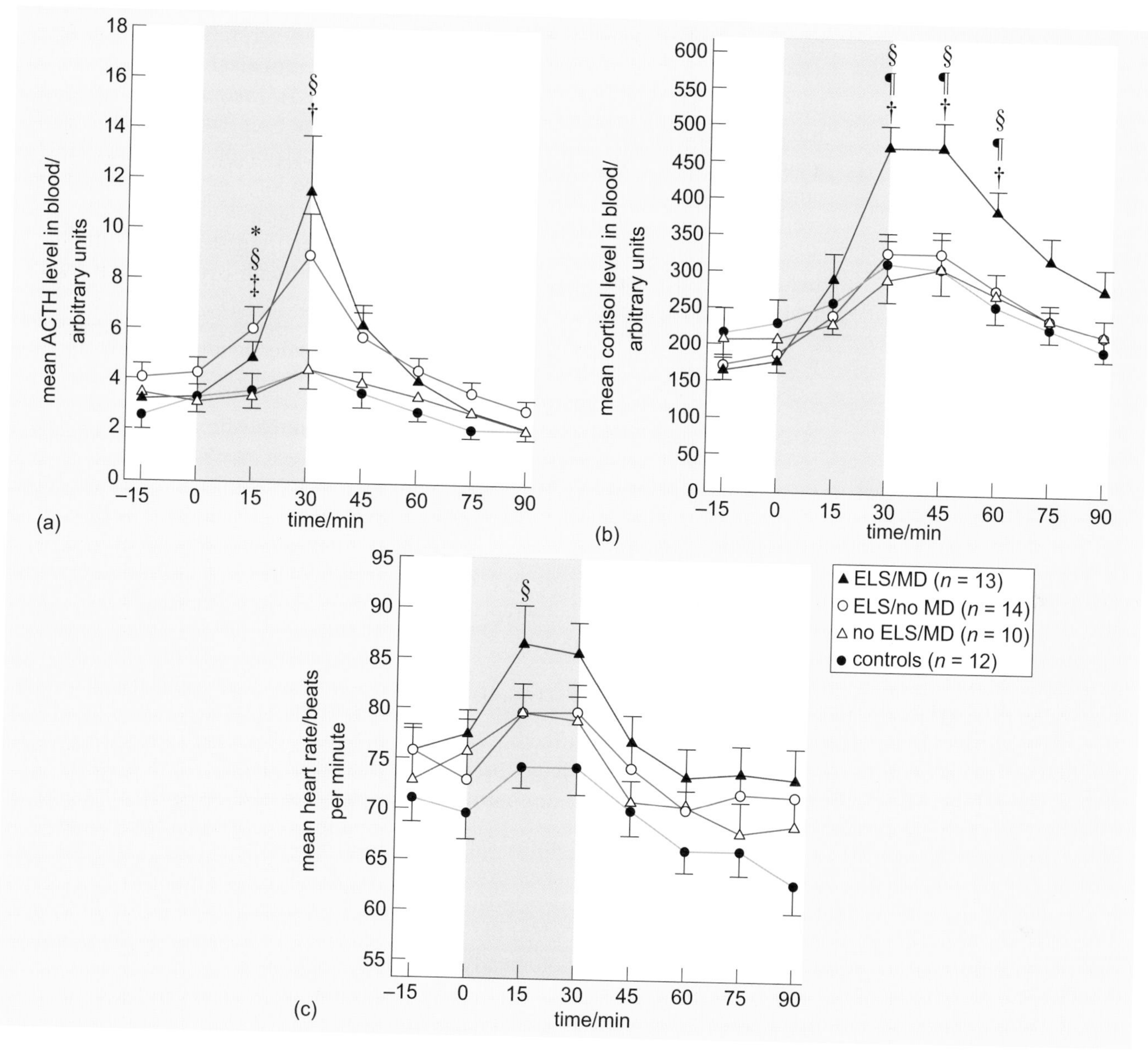

Figure 2.3 Mean levels (±SEMs) of (a) adrenocorticotropic hormone, ACTH, and (b) cortisol, in the blood; (c) heart rate in women who underwent a Trier social stress test. The shaded area shows the duration of the Trier test. Statistically significant differences between groups are indicated on the figure as follows: * between controls and ELS/no MD; § between controls and ELS/MD; ‡ between ELS/no MD and no ELS/MD; † between ELS/MD and no ELS/MD; ¶ between ELS/no MD and ELS/MD.

2.2.4 Cognition and stress

Psychologists suggest that there are cognitive styles, or ways of thinking, that predispose people to stress and therefore the development of anxiety and depression.

Cognitive appraisals

Selye's concept of stress, and the idea that 'it is how you take it' that is important, informed the work of the eminent American psychologist Richard

Lazarus. Lazarus suggested that how an individual interprets or evaluates an event or situation – a cognitive process he called **appraisal** – plays a critical part in feeling stressed (Lazarus and Folkman, 1984). Imagine that you are travelling in a desert and find your water bottle has been leaking. Half the water is gone: a classic 'Is the bottle half full or half empty?' scenario. The amount of water in the bottle is a constant, but one kind of evaluation could well lead to more stress and panic than the other. Lazarus and his colleagues also suggested that people are more likely to suffer from stress when they believe that they lack the resources to deal with difficult events than if they feel confident that they have the resources to cope.

■ How is the concept of appraisal relevant to understanding and treating emotional disorders?

□ First, it highlights the fact that unhelpful or unrealistic appraisals, rather than particular events or situations in themselves, can cause stress. Second, it holds out hope, as appraisals and styles of appraisal may be amenable to change.

Challenging and re-framing appraisals is a crucial part of some of the strategies used by psychotherapists to help people with emotional disorders (Chapter 3).

Helplessness and lack of control

An important element affecting how stressed individuals feel is how much control they think they have: people feel more anxious and frustrated if they feel they cannot predict or control a situation or get the outcomes they want.

The effect of 'lack of control' has been studied experimentally in rats. A rat that cannot control (by lever pressing, as it has been trained to do) an electric shock, first becomes hypervigilant and presses the pedal wildly to try to control the shock even when the shock is not actually being delivered: it is in a state of anxiety. Physiologically, this state is characterised by acute activation of the stress response, involving secretion of adrenalin and noradrenalin, as well as increased secretion of corticosterone (the rat version of cortisol) (Book 1, Section 3.2).

If the shocks continue and no 'coping' response by the rat has any affect whatsoever on the likelihood of receiving a shock, it stops lever-pressing or trying to exert control in any way. The critical finding is that when later placed in a situation where shock is avoidable, such an animal becomes inactive and appears unable to learn strategies for avoiding the shock. Seligman (1992 [1975]) termed this state 'learned helplessness'.

This kind of helplessness or hopelessness resembles that of subordinate, defeated non-human animals in status hierarchies (Section 1.3.5). In humans, it is easy to see how it might arise in an abused child, or in a woman experiencing domestic violence. As we saw in Section 1.3.5, circumstances of entrapment and humiliation seem particularly potent in their capacity to trigger severe depression.

2.2.5 Temperament, personality and heritability

Some people seem to have easy-going temperaments and to remain unruffled by the kinds of events or situations that leave others tense and fraught, or upset and tearful. Responses to life events, and differences in cognitive interpretation of negative events, have therefore been linked to personality factors (Hirschfeld and Shea, 1992). Here, personality is understood to mean a person's attitudes and beliefs as well as aspects of temperament which can be very stable. Think back, for instance, to 'trait anxiety', discussed in Section 1.2.1.

There is evidence that personality traits are associated with affective and anxiety disorders. For instance neuroticism, the tendency to be emotionally unstable (Box 1.2), predisposes to anxiety and depression, while having an easy-going temperament seems to protect against depression (Clark et al., 1994). Also, there is evidence that those who are very dependent on the approval of others, need to maintain tight control of everything, are impulsive or easily angered, cope less effectively with stressors.

All these personality characteristics may result in situations that make life even worse – think of the young man who is quick to anger and assaults a traffic warden who is giving him a parking ticket. He may end up in court, his own actions having landed him in a yet more stressful situation. Thus personality factors have the potential to mediate the relationship between stress and the development of emotional disorders.

Inheritance of temperament

Why do people have such different temperaments? Our early experiences may well make a significant contribution, for instance the evidence that nurturing can affect how anxious an animal becomes is discussed in Section 2.4.2. However, genetic inheritance undoubtedly contributes to temperamental characteristics.

This is most clearly shown by experiments on animals. A fascinating experiment started in 1959 by the Russian geneticist Dmitri Belayev to tame captive-bred red foxes provides a good illustration of the fact that genetic inheritance affects temperament. In foxes, as in humans, there is variation in temperamental traits, with different individuals behaving differently. Most captive red foxes were either ferociously aggressive towards humans or afraid of them, but a small proportion showed neither of these traits – they showed the desirable trait of lack of fear and aggression towards humans.

In the experimental population, only those foxes that showed this desirable trait were selected for breeding. After repeating the process for 10 generations, 18% of the foxes in the experimental population were tame and happy to be with humans (Figure 2.4). They approached and licked people, wagged their tails, whined and begged for food. After 20 generations (40 years and 45 000 foxes later!), 35% were tame. The increasing proportion that exhibited the selected trait provided clear evidence that temperamental traits are heritable (Trut, 1999). The proportion showing the trait in the 'control' population remained low throughout the study.

Genes affecting one character are often linked to genes affecting other characters, and can be passed on together – that is, genetic inheritance is complex in its effects.

Intriguingly, the genes mediating tameness also mediated a dramatic change in the appearance of the foxes. As Figure 2.4c shows, their coat colours and markings became very similar to those of domestic dogs such as border collies (Figure 2.4d).

Figure 2.4 Photos of (a) a wild fox, (b) and (c) foxes bred to be tame and (d) a border collie, illustrating the change in markings on the tame foxes to resemble border collies.

You may feel surprised that, although Belayev and his colleagues bred only from foxes showing the 'tameness' trait, after 40 years only around one-third of the experimental population were 'tame'. In fact, this is not really surprising as a trait of this kind is complex. It is linked to the activity not just of one gene but a whole constellation of genes. It is highly likely that many different genes contribute to the trait of 'lack of fear and aggression towards humans', and need to be inherited from its parents for an individual to manifest the trait. By analogy, getting one winning number on a lottery ticket is very common, but to win a substantial prize you need to get many or all numbers correct at the same time, and that is a much rarer occurrence.

Familial inheritance and heritability in humans

Temperamental characteristics and mental disorders frequently run in families. Thus the close blood relatives (children, siblings and parents) of patients with major depression or bipolar disorder are much more likely to suffer from these conditions than people from the general population.

How can it be ascertained what contribution genetic factors make to such disorders? One way is to look at what combinations of genetic factors make it more likely that a person will be vulnerable to environmental factors such as stressful events, and hence to developing disorders such as depression. This approach is discussed later, in Section 2.4.1.

Another way is to look in detail at precisely how genetic factors act on the brain and body to make a disorder more likely, and some of the exciting work in this area, which has been carried out largely on animals, is considered in Section 2.4.2.

Here we restrict ourselves to considering, briefly, the issue of **heritability** (Box 2.1), which attempts to give a numeric value to the contribution genetic factors make to the development of particular traits or mental health conditions.

Box 2.1 Heritability

Heritability is a measure of how much of the variation between individuals in a given character is due to differences in their genes, rather than to differences in their environments, in a particular population. It is expressed as a number between 0 (definitely not due to differences in genes) and 1 (wholly due to differences in genes). It can also be expressed as a percentage, from 0% to 100%. Note that a heritability of 0.4 for a disorder such as depression does not mean that 40% of cases of depression are caused by genes, or even that a specific individual's depression is 40% due to genes. Every case is caused by genes and the environment in combination. The heritability figure of 0.4 means that, within the study population, 40% of the variation in whether people get depression or not is due to differences in their genes.

Trying to put a figure on genetic contributions to characteristics that run in families is, of course, complicated by the fact that inheritance in families can arise from social learning or culture. For instance, the children of Christians tend to be Christians, while those of Muslims tend to be Muslims, but the inheritance of religious affiliation is clearly sociocultural rather than genetic, so in this case heritability is 0 (or 0%) (Box 2.1).

In many other situations, the relative contribution of genes and environment is much less obvious. Epidemiologists who are interested in the genetic basis of disorders have a number of strategies to overcome this difficulty. One important approach is to look at the incidence of a disorder amongst sets of identical twins. Identical twins inherit the same genes from their parents, so any differences between them are likely to be due to environmental effects. Adoption studies involving identical twins have proved invaluable in disentangling genetic and environmental influences.

- ■ Imagine that a study of identical twins adopted into very different family environments at birth showed that as adults: (i) they were very similar in character X; (ii) they were very different in character Y. Explain, with reasons, what this suggests about the heritability of characters X and Y.

- ☐ The environment in which the identical twins were raised was very different but their genetic inheritance was the same, so (i) suggests that *genes* had most impact on the development of character X (i.e. X has high heritability); (ii) suggests that the *environment* had most impact on the development of character Y (i.e. Y has low heritability).

Using approaches such as these, genetic epidemiologists have estimated that the heritability of major depression is 31%–42% (Sullivan et al., 2000). The heritabilities of anxiety disorders such as GAD, OCD, specific phobias and panic disorder have a similar range, from 30% to 40% (Smoller et al., 2008). For comparison, the heritabilities of schizophrenia and bipolar disorder are estimated to be 50%–70%.

Their heritability values suggest that both major depression and anxiety disorders are multicausal, since both genetic and environmental factors make substantial contributions. Genetic influences, and the interaction of genetic and environmental factors, will be considered further in Section 2.4.

But first we will look in more detail at the biological stress response.

2.2.6 Stress and the brain

Following on from the consideration of stressful life events, and in the knowledge that such events are often linked to the development of depression and anxiety, in this section we look more closely at the biological stress response and its effects on the brain.

The hypothalamic–pituitary–adrenal axis and hyperactivity

The stress response evolved as a coordinated survival reaction to stimuli perceived to be threatening. As you saw in Book 1 (Section 3.2.1), there are two strands to the stress response. One elicits extremely rapid responses to cope with an emergency. This operates via the SNS and triggers the release of hormones such as adrenalin, which increases alertness. It also increases heart rate so that blood, and the oxygen and nutrients it carries, gets to muscles used in running or fighting quickly.

The response is triggered in the first instance by the amygdala, which is of central importance in emotional perception and behaviour, and this can result in the detection of the potential threat and danger before we are consciously aware of it (Section 1.3.2). (Of course, in some cases, conscious consideration may convince us that there was no real threat!) The amygdala releases CRF (corticotropin-releasing factor) to stimulate the response from the SNS.

CRF release from the amygdala also triggers the second strand of the stress response – here the CRF signal from the amygdala goes to a brain region called the hypothalamus. The hypothalamus then itself releases CRF as a signal to the pituitary gland, which in turn releases the hormone ACTH (adrenocorticotropic hormone) into the blood circulation. The main function of ACTH is to signal to the adrenal glands to begin releasing corticosteroids into the blood. This system is called the **HPA (hypothalamic–pituitary–adrenal) axis** (Figure 2.5; see also Book 1, Figure 3.4).

- ■ Book 1, Section 3.2.1 mentions a corticosteroid secreted by the adrenal gland – can you recall what it is?
- □ Cortisol. This is a corticosteroid secreted in humans. In rats, the equivalent is called corticosterone.

If the response is effective (that is, the stressor disappears, or after conscious reflection is judged not to be a danger after all), then body and mind calm down: both the SNS response and the HPA axis become less active, allowing adrenalin levels, heart rate and cortisol levels to return to normal. However, if an external stressor remains, or if an individual continues to feel threatened, the stress response is prolonged and stress becomes chronic.

Cortisol and corticosterone are examples of corticosteroids. These are also called glucocorticoids as they affect glucose metabolism.

The effects of prolonged activation of the HPA axis by stressors are of particular interest for understanding depression and anxiety, hence this strand of the stress response will be considered further.

The glucocorticoids produced as a result of HPA axis activity perform a vital function. They mobilise the body's fat and other energy reserves for release into the bloodstream, where they are then available to sustain the high-energy needs of an individual should there be a prolonged struggle or flight. However, glucocorticoids are damaging to neurons and other cells if present for long periods and in high concentrations. Thus it is important that levels of glucocorticoids are brought back to normal or 'baseline' levels as soon as possible.

A mechanism exists to control the level of glucocorticoids and to switch off further production if it is too high. This mechanism involves the hypothalamus, the hippocampus and the prefrontal cortex (all of which you met in Section 1.3.2). Neurons in these brain areas carry special receptors called **glucocorticoid receptors (GRs)**, to which glucocorticoids such as cortisol and corticosterone attach when they are released into the bloodstream. In Activity 2.1, you will see how glucocorticoid receptors play a crucial part in controlling the HPA axis and hence the stress response, and you will also see what happens when this control fails under conditions of chronic stress.

Figure 2.5 shows the HPA axis, its links to brain areas such as amygdala, the hippocampus and the prefrontal cortex, and the locations of the GRs.

Activity 2.1 Stress and the operation and control of the hypothalamic–pituitary–adrenal (HPA) axis

(LO 2.2) Allow 1.5 hours

Now would be an ideal time to study Activity 2.1 in the multimedia map. The first part of the activity includes a video clip illustrating the experience of stress and situations that elicit the stress response.

The second part of the activity is an interactive animation and is designed to help you understand the operation of the HPA axis – how it is controlled under normal conditions and how the controls are disrupted under conditions of chronic stress.

This activity will help you appreciate the nature of stress and the role played by stress and the HPA axis when we come to consider the aetiology of emotional disorders such as depression and anxiety.

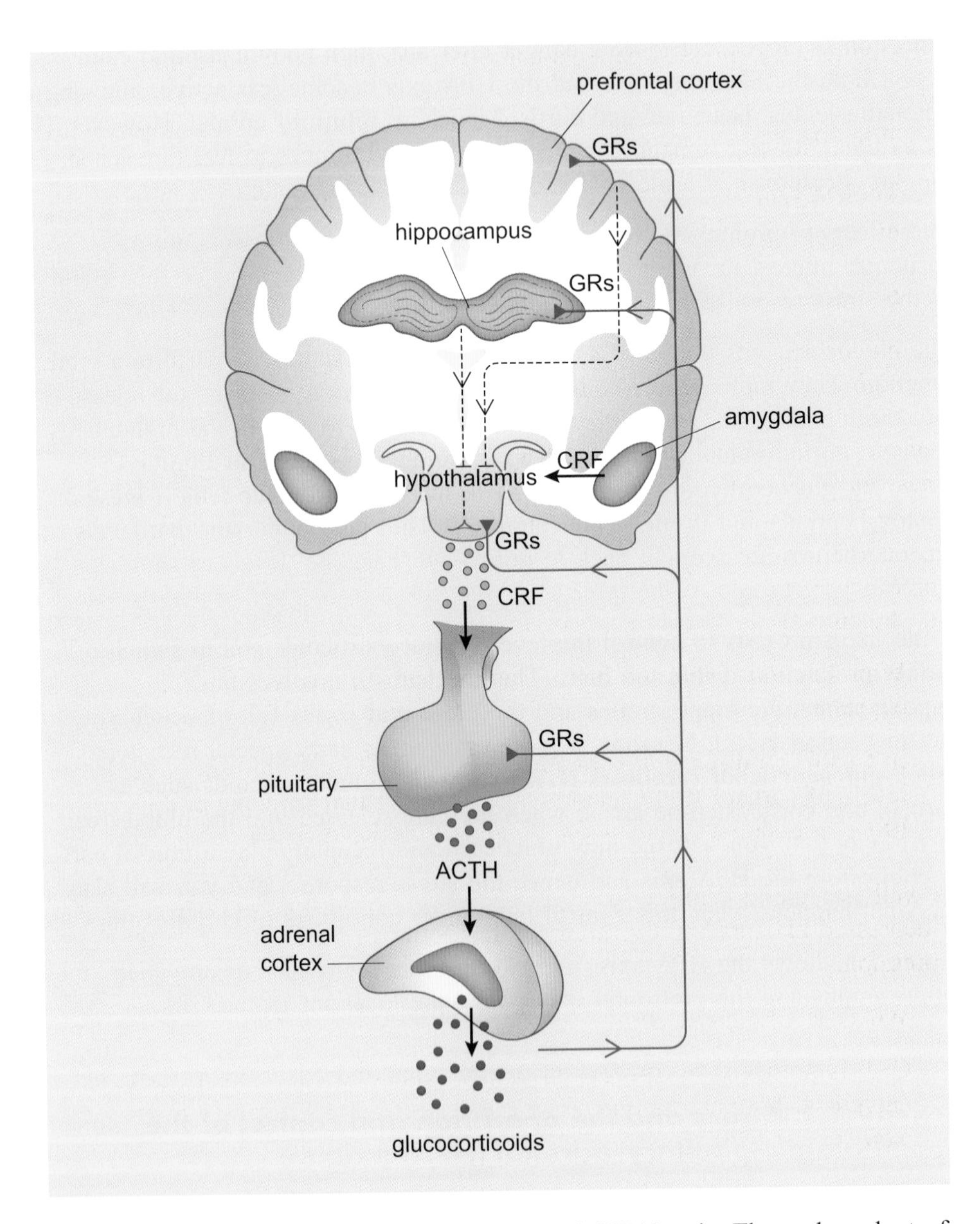

Figure 2.5 The hypothalamic–pituitary–adrenal (HPA) axis. The end-product of a cascade of events is the release of glucocorticoids (such as cortisol) which travel via the bloodstream and attach to glucocorticoid receptors (GRs, shown as green triangles). The dashed lines show neural connections via which the prefrontal cortex and the hippocampus can influence the activity of the hypothalamus. CRF: corticotropin releasing factor; ACTH: adrenocorticotropic hormone.

Relating stress and depression biologically

Evidence from studies on humans suggests that dysregulation (the breakdown of regulation) of the HPA axis due to chronic activation of the axis is linked to depression.

For instance, high levels of cortisol are found in the urine, blood and **cerebrospinal fluid (CSF)** (the fluid that bathes the brain and spinal cord) of many untreated depressed patients compared to controls who are not depressed.

■ What do high levels of cortisol suggest?

□ They suggest *hyperactivity* in the HPA axis of those who are depressed, as cortisol levels are high and uncontrolled.

■ Do these results tell us if high levels of cortisol cause depression?

□ No – they tell us there is a correlation. The depression might have led to high cortisol levels, rather than vice versa.

However some evidence that high levels of glucocorticoids such as cortisol can actually *cause* low mood in people is provided by Cushing's disease. This disease is sometimes caused by a tumour in the pituitary gland, which consequently secretes extra ACTH, which then stimulates the adrenal cortex to secrete more cortisol. If the level of cortisol is reduced (for instance by using drug treatment), the depression lifts.

■ Why does this suggest a causal role for high levels of cortisol in depression?

□ In Cushing's disease, the direction of causation is fairly certain: high levels of cortisol lead to depression. The fact that reducing cortisol levels lifts depression strengthens the case that cortisol plays a causal role.

As well as high cortisol levels, CRF concentrations in the cerebrospinal fluid of depressed patients are also high, compared to those who do not have depression.

■ Where is CRF produced?

□ CRF is produced by neurons in the hypothalamus, and also in the amygdala; both are involved in activating the stress response in the HPA axis.

This fits in with the finding from post-mortem studies that the brains of people with depression have more CRF-producing neurons in the hypothalamus compared to controls. Moreover, if CRF is injected into the brains of rats, these animals show some behaviours characteristic of depression such as insomnia, decreased appetite, decreased interest in sex, and increased anxiety (Arborelius et al., 1999). All these findings lend weight to the idea that hyperactivity in the HPA axis plays a causal role in depression and anxiety.

Effects on the hippocampus and prefrontal cortex

As you will have seen from Activity 2.1, the constant barrage of glucocorticoids during chronic stress is deleterious for glucocorticoid receptors, which play a critical role in controlling the stress response. Uncontrolled, high levels of glucocorticoids are also thought to weaken neurons in the hippocampus and the prefrontal cortex, making them more susceptible to damage or death.

■ Based on what you learned about these brain structures in Activity 2.1, what would be the psychological effect of: (a) hippocampal damage; (b) prefrontal cortex damage, of the kind caused by HPA hyperactivity?

□ (a) It might affect our ability to retrieve conscious memories of facts or events or the ability to form new ones; (b) It would become more difficult to make judgements and decisions; to concentrate on a task in hand, and to exert conscious control over behaviour, thoughts or impulses.

There is evidence from brain imaging data that the volume of the hippocampus, and of areas in the prefrontal cortex, is lower in people with depression (Campbell et al., 2004; Drevets et al., 1997). There is also evidence that activity in the prefrontal cortex is reduced in areas that are thought to be implicated in the control of emotions (Drevets, 1998). Via its effects on the hippocampus and the prefrontal cortex, stress may thus cause some of the symptoms of depression, such as difficulties in learning, remembering and concentrating, and the inability to control negative thoughts and emotions (cf. Lewis Wolpert's account (Vignette 1.1) and diagnostic criterion 8 in Box 1.5).

As we also saw in Lewis Wolpert's account, and in Section 1.5.2, depression and anxiety are often comorbid. So it is not surprising that anxiety too has links to stress, as considered in the next section.

Relating stress and anxiety biologically

Anxiety is linked to fear, and the amygdala plays a central role in attaching emotional significance to what we perceive and 'deciding' if fear, and hence 'fight or flight', is an appropriate reaction (Section 1.3.2). It is important for animals to remember threatening situations and to avoid them, hence the amygdala also plays a crucial role in consolidating and storing memories of emotionally arousing, stressful experiences, including unconscious fear memories.

As you saw above, it is the amygdala that initiates the stress response. But how is it itself affected by the consequences of that stress, and how might this be linked to anxiety?

A part of the amygdala, the basolateral amygdala (BLA), is well supplied with glucocorticoid receptors, raising the possibility that the amygdala could be directly affected by a rise in glucocorticoid levels following stress.

Mitra and Sapolsky (2008) injected rats with high doses of corticosterone (the rat glucocorticoid) for 1 day to represent acute stress. The corticosterone was dissolved in a 'vehicle', that is, a neutral carrier fluid. Control rats did not receive any corticosterone – they were injected with just the vehicle. (For more about the importance of controls and their treatment, see Box 2.2.)

Of interest to us here is that 12 days after the end of the treatments Mitra and Sapolsky (2008) carried out the following:

(A) They compared neurons from the amygdalas of treated rats with neurons from the amygdalas of control rats. Rats treated with corticosterone had sprouted more **dendrites** in their amygdala neurons than had the controls (Figure 2.6a).

(B) They compared treated and control rats on behavioural measures of anxiety, using an elevated plus maze (Figure 2.6b). In this kind of maze, rats that are anxious tend to stay in the closed arms and avoid the open arms, which are more exposed. Rats who had received corticosterone showed increased anxiety, spending less time on the open arms compared to control rats (Figure 2.6c).

Dendrites are thin, relatively short tubes (i.e. not the axon) sprouting from a neuron. They are important structures on neurons as it is dendrites that receive signals (or synaptic inputs) from other neurons.

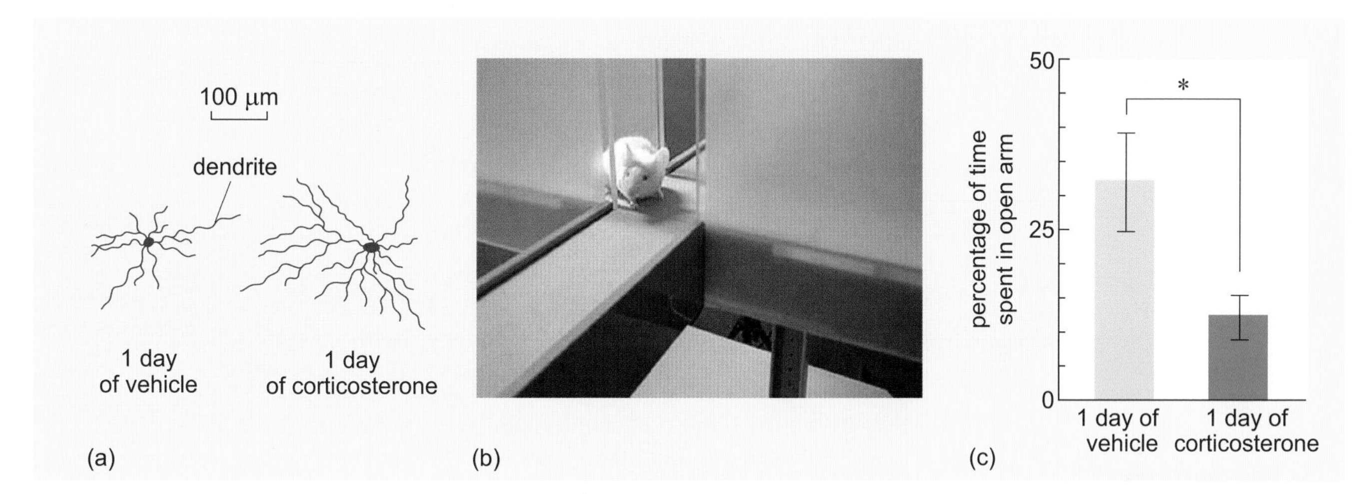

Figure 2.6 (a) Neurons in the amygdala of rats which received corticosterone sprouted more dendrites compared to neurons in the amygdala of rats in the control group, which just received the vehicle. (b) The elevated plus maze is used to test how anxious rats or mice are, by measuring how long they spend on open as opposed to closed arms of the maze. (c) Measure of anxiety in the elevated plus maze: rats who received corticosterone spent less time on the open arms of the elevated plus maze compared to control rats who received the vehicle. The asterisk denotes that the difference seen was statistically significant. The values shown are the mean ±SEM.

Thus a short period of intense 'stress' proved sufficient to trigger a marked response in the amygdala, as suggested by the neuronal sprouting. The 'stress' was also sufficient to induce long-term anxiety – in this case for at least 12 days, which is a significant period in the life of a rat.

Much is still not known about the workings of the amygdala, or about how brain systems affect one another in times of stress. However, it is tempting to speculate that the kind of effect described above is relevant to disorders such as post-traumatic stress disorder (PTSD), which can result from a single, traumatic event.

Chronic stress (represented by prolonged corticosterone application to rats) also 'boosts' dendrite formation in the amygdala in a similar way to that shown for acute stress (Mitra and Sapolsky, 2008).

Clearly the amygdala is profoundly structurally changed by stress, and as you will see below, this leads to it exerting a more powerful influence on other parts of the brain.

The more dendrites a neuron has, the more signals (or synaptic inputs) from other neurons it can receive. The new BLA dendrites described above grow glutamate receptors which are hypersensitive to excitatory inputs from other areas of the brain (Chattarji, 2008).

Some drugs (such as benzodiazepines) prescribed to reduce anxiety bind to GABA receptors and reinforce the effects of GABA (see Chapter 3).

The amygdala is also rich in receptors for the inhibitory neurotransmitter GABA. Stress is known to lower levels of GABA and hence GABA inhibition on the amygdala (Roozendaal et al., 2009). (Glutamate is the main excitatory neurotransmitter in the brain, and GABA is the main inhibitory neurotransmitter in the brain (Book 1, Section 2.3.2).)

- ■ How will stress affect the overall activity of the amygdala, given the above? Explain your reasoning.
- □ An increase in glutamatergic input will excite the amygdala. If GABA inhibition is reduced, the brake on excitation will become weaker. Hence there will be an overall increase in the activity and excitability of the amygdala.

The results of studies done on rodents described above may thus explain findings from brain imaging studies in humans which suggest that the amygdala is over-active in those with anxiety and depression (Drevets, 1998).

A hyperactive amygdala may contribute to the well-established vividness of emotionally significant memories, as the amygdala sends powerful inputs to the hippocampus to give emotional flavour to conscious memories. A more active amygdala, via its triggering effects on the HPA axis, might also intensify the stress response further. It might also underlie the emotional symptoms seen in affective and anxiety disorders.

Next, the amygdala's activity in humans with generalised anxiety disorder (GAD) is considered.

Box 2.2 Research Methods: Variables in an experiment

In Mitra and Sapolsky's experiment (Section 2.2.6), rats were divided into two groups: those who received glucocorticoids and those who did not.

- ■ What are the dependent and independent variables in the experiment shown in Figure 2.6c? (Dependent and independent variables are considered in Book 1, Box 2.1.)

□ The dependent variable is the percentage of time spent in open arm exploration. The independent variable is corticosterone treatment. There are two **conditions** in this experiment: (1) treatment with corticosterone; (2) no corticosterone treatment.

As well as the dependent and independent variables, there are many other variables, known as **extraneous variables**, present in an experiment. For instance, in the above experiment extraneous variables might include the feeding or sleeping behaviour of the rats, the temperature in the laboratory, or the time of day that recordings are made. Researchers try to keep such factors as constant as possible during experiments; for instance, by keeping all animals in similar surroundings and taking measurements at particular times of day.

An important part of designing an experiment is to ensure that extraneous variables do not become **confounding variables**: in other words, that they don't vary systematically with the independent variable and therefore interfere with the results of the experiment. This can be illustrated with an example from the rat experiment mentioned above. Suppose that rats in the experimental condition received an injection of corticosterone and rats in the control condition received no treatment at all. Could you be sure that any difference in behaviour was due to the effects of corticosterone? What about the effects of the injection itself, or the effects of being handled by the experimenter? For this reason, it is necessary to give an injection to the control rats also, containing in this case only the inert substance used to dissolve the corticosterone (the 'vehicle'), so that any effects seen are due to the corticosterone. The aim of any experiment is to ensure that the independent variable is the only variable that differs systematically between the two conditions.

The amygdala and generalised anxiety disorder

There is some evidence that the amygdalas of people with generalised anxiety disorder (GAD) may be abnormally active, so that they feel anxious and fearful without apparent reason. For instance, Nitschke et al. (2009) recorded activity in the amygdalas of patients with GAD and controls without GAD as they looked at images of unpleasant objects such as mutilated bodies, or neutral objects such as fire hydrants.

A few seconds before seeing the images, all participants received a cue to let them know whether to expect an unpleasant or neutral photograph. Nitschke et al. (2009) found that the amygdala activation of those with GAD did *not* differ significantly from that of controls (without GAD) when they were *viewing* unpleasant or neutral images.

However, the amygdalas of GAD patients became much more active than those of controls when they were shown cues signalling that a negative or neutral image would be appearing (Figure 2.7).

■ What does this suggest?

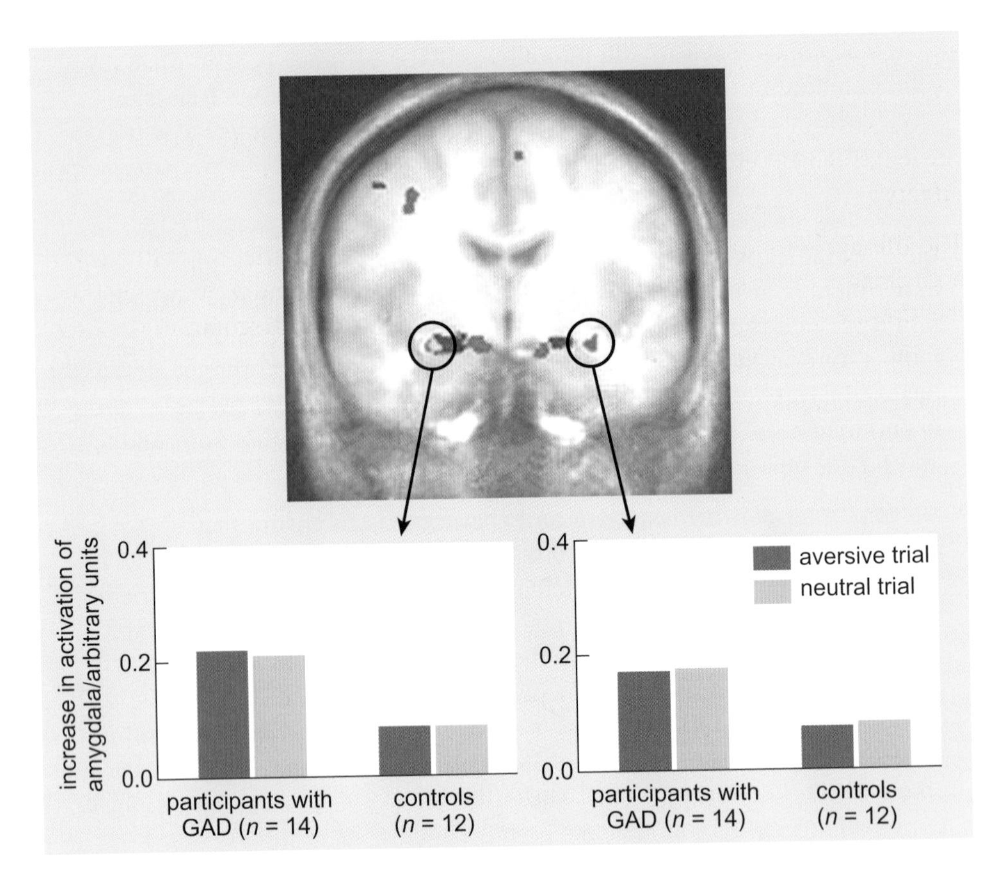

Figure 2.7 Anticipatory amygdala activation differentiating participants with generalised anxiety disorder (GAD) and healthy controls. Participants with GAD had significantly greater activation in the amygdala on both sides of the brain compared to healthy controls without GAD. This was the case both in aversive trials (in which a cue predicting an aversive image was presented) and in neutral trials (in which a cue predicting a neutral image was presented). (The amygdalas are circled.)

□ It suggests that anticipation stirs up a high level of activity in the amygdalas of those with GAD. They become abnormally anxious even when what is being anticipated is not in the least unpleasant.

Currently it is not known why the amygdalas of patients with GAD are over-active. As GAD has a heritability of 30%–40%, genetic factors clearly play some part. However, stress and its 'boosting' effect on the amygdala, discussed above, may also be important.

2.2.7 The life-cycle model of stress

As we have seen above, the overall picture emerging from studies of how stress affects the brain is that chronic or repeated exposure to stress can affect the structure of several areas of the brain via the action of glucocorticoids released during activation of the HPA axis.

The studies have been on animals and humans of different ages. Recently, researchers have begun to ask whether the effects of stressful or traumatic experiences depend on the *age* at which they occur. Developmental biologists have long known that environmental (including social) factors can have particularly long-lasting effects if experienced early in life or at other 'vulnerability periods'. Early effects, which can set an individual on a particular developmental path for life, have been described as '**programming effects**'.

The life-cycle model of stress proposes that stressful experiences will have a high impact on brain structures that are growing most rapidly at the time of the stress exposure (in young individuals), or that are undergoing age-related decline (in adult and old individuals).

As Figure 2.8 shows, in humans, different brain structures develop or reach maturity at different ages. This is certainly true of the three brain regions we have already identified as having an important role in the control of the HPA axis, and which are therefore of particular interest – the hippocampus, the prefrontal cortex and the amygdala.

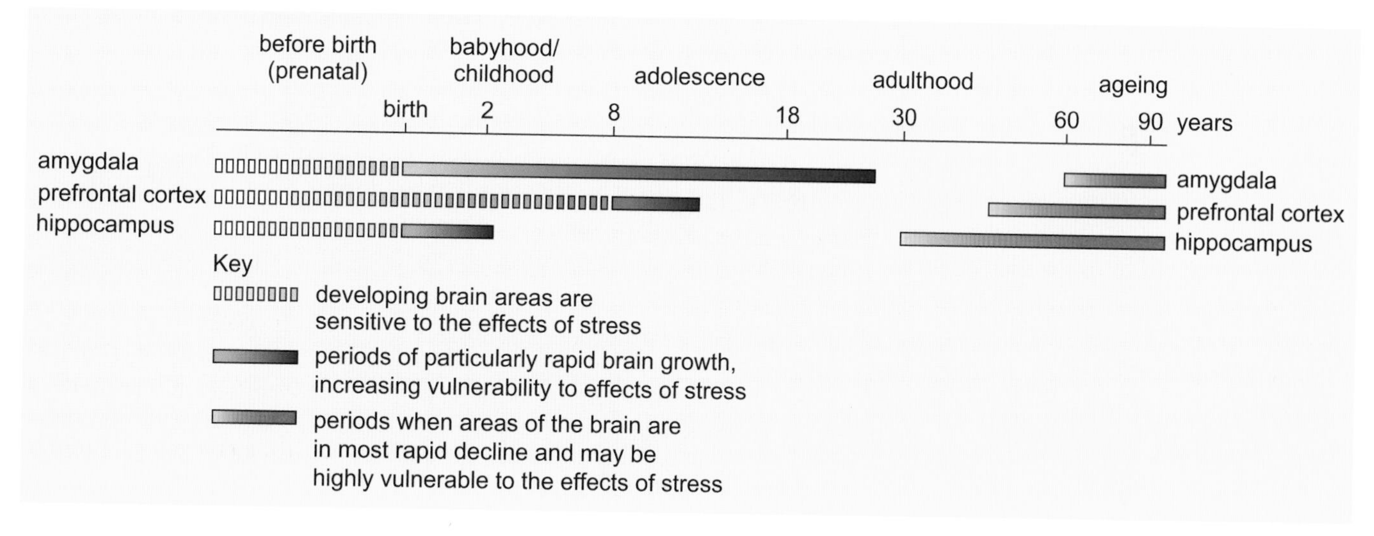

Figure 2.8 The effects of stress on the brain may in part depend on the stage of growth and development of particular brain areas during the human lifespan.

■ Which areas of the human brain are developing or growing rapidly in the period: (i) prenatally; (ii) from birth to 2 years; (iii) between 11 and 12 years?

□ (i) the hippocampus, prefrontal cortex and amygdala; (ii) the hippocampus and amygdala; (iii) the prefrontal cortex and the amygdala.

Effects on the hippocampus, which in humans is actively growing prenatally and after birth, have been of particular interest because of its importance in the control of the HPA axis.

Experiments in which rats are exposed to chronic or intense stress show that if stress occurs when rats are pups, damage to the hippocampus and the subsequent effects on behaviour are long-lasting and difficult to reverse. But if stress occurs in adulthood, the effects, even of chronic stress, are reversed after only a few weeks of non-stress.

Researchers wondered if there was a similar effect in humans, and if so whether it was related to depression. They were aware that there is a well-established association in humans between hippocampal size and depression: the hippocampus is smaller in people with depression than in non-depressed controls (Campbell et al., 2004).

This finding raises questions about how major depression is classified – see Box 2.3.

Remarkably, however, this association may exist because, lacking life-cycle data, researchers did not take into account the *age* at which stress was experienced. It turns out that only a subset of women with depression – those who have *also* experienced childhood abuse – may have a smaller hippocampus (review in Heim et al., 2008). Women who are depressed, but who have *not* experienced child abuse, have hippocampal sizes similar to controls (i.e. women who are not depressed and who have not experienced childhood abuse).

Box 2.3 Biologically distinct subtypes of major depression?

DSM IV-TR criteria (APA, 2000) for major depression (MD; Chapter 1) are based on *symptoms* rather than on aetiology. Researchers use MD diagnosed according to such criteria when exploring the correlates and aetiology of MD. However the results discussed in Heim et al. (2008) raise important questions about the classification of MD, as they suggest that two biologically distinct subtypes may be lumped together: depression associated with smaller hippocampus size (perhaps due to early trauma) and depression that is not associated with smaller hippocampus size. There may be other (currently unspecified) differences associated with these apparent subtypes.

This finding is consistent with data from experiments on rats that show early stress is linked to long-lasting damage to the hippocampus, and that stress-related hippocampal damage in adulthood is more easily reversed.

It is also consistent with age-related effects found by McCauley et al. (1997) in a study of more than 1900 women: they found that childhood, but not adulthood, sexual or physical abuse was a strong predictor of increases in depression and anxiety.

How might the link between child abuse and depression arise? In Activity 2.1, you saw that the undamaged hippocampus has an important role in controlling the HPA axis and calming the stress response. Early damage to the hippocampus, as a result of severe or prolonged stressful experiences such as childhood abuse, has potentially long-lasting effects on control of the stress response.

- Can you recall a human example from earlier in this chapter where adverse early experience was linked to an over-active stress response?

- □ Yes, women who had been abused as children had a stress response that was over-active during the Trier social stress test, compared to women who had not been abused in childhood (Section 2.2.3).

A poorly functioning hippocampus may thus be a 'vulnerability factor' or '**diathesis**', for depression when further stress is experienced. Such stress would trigger a badly controlled stress response which would further damage the hippocampus and other brain structures and could predispose to depression. Repeated episodes could lead to significant changes in the volume of the hippocampus and other brain areas.

- ■ Can you be sure that early life stress is the only factor contributing to small hippocampus size and dysfunction?
- □ No, you cannot. It is possible that other influences such as genetic factors also influence hippocampus size and dysfunction.

The life-cycle approach thus promises to add a valuable perspective to research on the aetiology of affective and anxiety disorders, as a very brief consideration of another example, to conclude this section, will confirm.

Hall (1998) suggested that if different parts of the brain are vulnerable to stressful, adverse circumstances at different ages, different mental disorders might be associated with stressful experiences at different ages. Thus stress at the time of rapid hippocampal development might lead to different emotional disorders than stress at times of rapid prefrontal cortex development.

Some recent human data seem to offer support for this hypothesis: women who experienced trauma before the age of 12 years had increased risk for major depression, whereas women who experienced trauma between 12 and 18 years of age more frequently developed PTSD (Maercker et al, 2004).

More longitudinal studies of individuals are clearly needed to explore fully the potential of the life-cycle approach.

Adaptive value of developmental programming of stress

It has been tacitly assumed above that the effects of stress on the brain are disadvantageous. However, there is another view, which makes sense if we consider brains as 'survival machines' that evolved to be moulded by experience. Our ancestors must have experienced stress and difficulty in their early lives, so it seems plausible that the developing brain evolved to cope with maltreatment.

On this view, early stress might trigger *adaptive* changes in the brain – changes that allow an individual to survive and reproduce in a dangerous world. Thus, an intense 'fight or flight' response, and constant alertness, might be exactly what is needed in some circumstances. This programme or strategy might give an individual an advantage in a dangerous, unpredictable environment.

Unfortunately, there is a dark side to this postulated adaptation as high levels of vigilance and stress-responsiveness do physiological and psychological damage – in humans they are associated with hypertension, obesity, increased risk of suicide, accelerated aging and degeneration of brain structures, including the hippocampus. However, if survival and reproduction were enhanced by this strategy more than by the 'laid-back' alternative, the strategy would have been favoured in some situations.

From what has been described so far about stress in Section 2.2, it is clear that an understanding of the effects of stress on the brain sheds a valuable light on the aetiology of depression and anxiety. But this is not the only knowledge of brain function that is important in this regard, as we shall now see.

2.3 Insights from antidepressants

As often happens in science, research into *how* the drugs work happened after the discovery that they *did* work.

Antidepressant drugs (also known as **antidepressant medications** or **ADMs**) were discovered completely by accident in the 1950s, starting a revolution in the treatment of affective disorders. The fact that they were effective in helping many people who were depressed led to a major research effort to find out how they worked.

This research has led to a number of influential hypotheses that attempt to explain the brain bases of such disorders. We shall consider three of these hypotheses here: the monoamine hypothesis, the neurotrophic hypothesis and the network hypothesis.

2.3.1 The monoamine hypothesis of mood disorders

Reserpine was isolated in 1952 from the dried root of *Rauwolfia serpentina*, a species of flowering plant also known as sarpaganda or 'snakeroot' in India. It was an ancient remedy for insanity, fever and snakebite. Apparently Gandhi used it as a tranquilliser.

In the 1950s it was noticed that around 20% of patients prescribed the drug reserpine, used at the time to control high blood pressure, developed severe depression as a side effect.

It was subsequently discovered that reserpine depletes a group of neurotransmitters called **monoamines**, which include serotonin, noradrenalin and dopamine. It works by preventing monoamines from being taken up into **vesicles**, leaving them vulnerable to being broken down in the cell. (Vesicles are small 'bubbles' in the **presynaptic** neuron in which neurotransmitter is stored before release into the **synaptic gap**, the gap between the presynaptic neuron and the **postsynaptic** neuron – see Figure 2.9.)

■ What are the consequences if reserpine stops monoamine neurotransmitter molecules from entering vesicles?

□ More monoamine neurotransmitter molecules are destroyed, so fewer are available for release into the synaptic gap, to bind to receptors on the post-synaptic cell. So neurotransmission is hampered – cells are not able to signal to one another as effectively.

Around the same time it was noticed that tuberculosis patients, prescribed a different drug, isoniazid, sometimes experienced a *lifting* of pre-existing depression. Isoniazid inhibits the enzyme **monoamine oxidase (MAO)** which breaks down monoamines.

■ What effect would inhibition of MAO have on neurotransmission involving monoamines such as serotonin and noradrenalin?

□ As MAO destroys monoamines, inhibiting MAO would increase the levels of monoamines available. Thus it would enhance neurotransmission.

Such **monoamine oxidase inhibitors (MAOIs)** became the first generation of antidepressants.

Subsequently it emerged that there was yet another way that available monoamine levels might increase: imipramine, another antidepressant, inhibited the *reuptake,* into the presynaptic neuron, of serotonin and noradrenalin that had been released into the synaptic gap (Figure 2.9; reuptake is introduced in Book 1, Section 2.3.2).

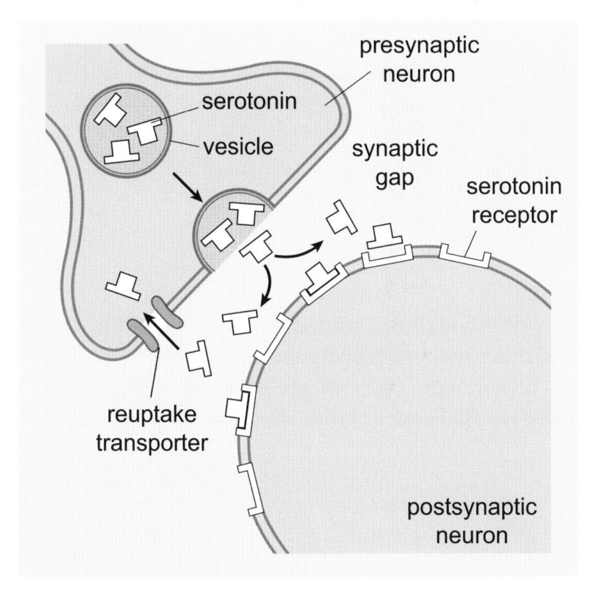

Figure 2.9 The serotonin synapse. Serotonin secreted by a presynaptic neuron into the synaptic gap binds to receptors on the postsynaptic neuron to affect the activity of the postsynaptic neuron. The postsynaptic neuron's response depends on the amount of serotonin in the synaptic gap. Serotonin levels in the synaptic gap fall partly because reuptake transporters take back the neurotransmitter into the presynaptic neuron.

■ What effect would inhibition of reuptake have on neurotransmission involving monoamines such as serotonin and noradrenalin?

□ It would increase the amount of monoamines in the synaptic gap, so it would enhance neurotransmission.

These findings about monoamines caused much excitement and led to the **monoamine hypothesis of mood disorders**. This postulated that monoamine levels have a *primary* role in causing depression, as lowering the levels of monoamines causes depression, while raising them lifts depression (see Hirschfeld (2000) for an overview). The mechanism postulated for this is shown in Figure 2.10.

■ Which model, biomedical or biopsychosocial, does the monoamine hypothesis exemplify?

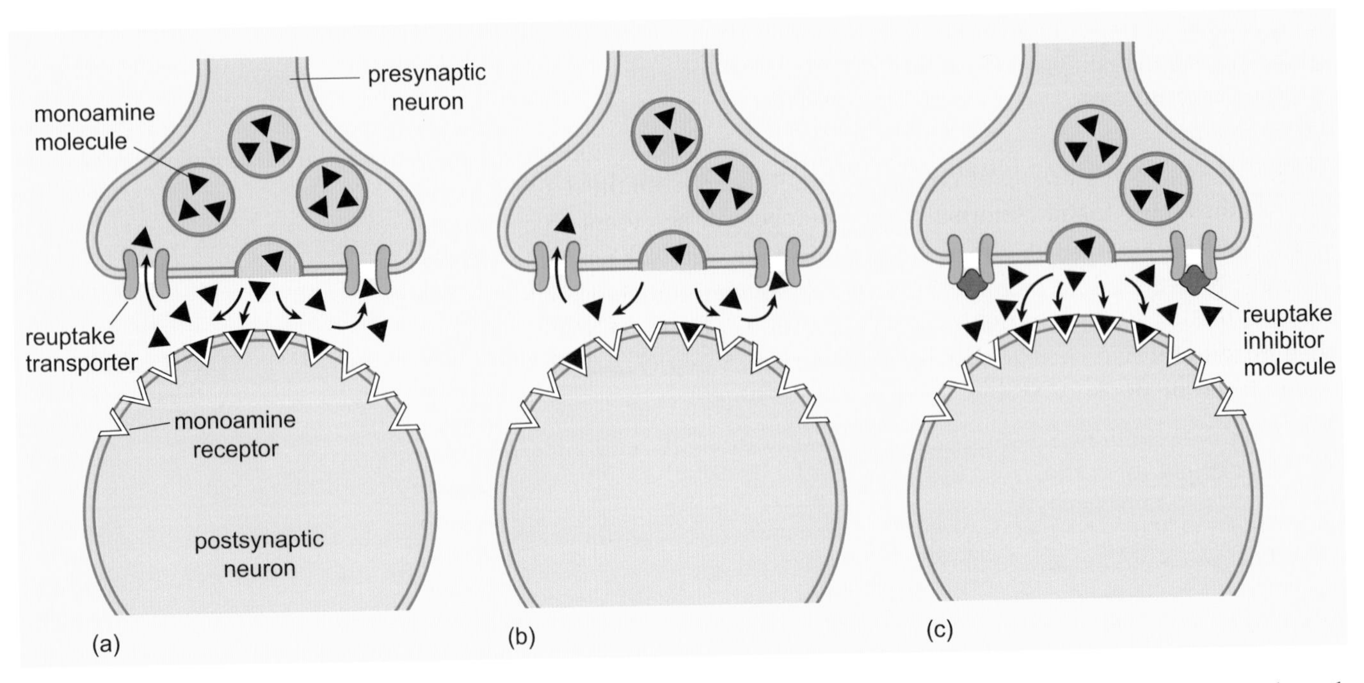

Figure 2.10 The monoamine hypothesis of mood disorders. (a) In normal brain, monoamine molecules are released and bind to receptors on the postsynaptic neuron; (b) In depression, fewer monoamine molecules are available for binding to receptors on the postsynaptic neuron, leading to a mood disorder; (c) Treatment with a reuptake inhibitor (the red shape blocking the reuptake transporter; here the SSRI Prozac®) increases the number of monoamine molecules in the synaptic gap, so more are available to bind to receptors on the postsynaptic neuron. This corrects the mood disorder.

□ The biomedical model: if depression is caused by a simple depletion of monoamines, it is tempting to think that drugs that raise the levels of monoamines in the brain can cure depression.

ADMs that inhibit the reuptake of specific monoamines such as serotonin (SSRIs, selective serotonin reuptake inhibitors, Book 1, Section 2.4.1), noradrenalin (noradrenergic reuptake inhibitors, NRIs), or combinations of monoamines such as serotonin and noradrenalin (serotonin noradrenergic reuptake inhibitors, SNRIs) are nowadays amongst the most prescribed drugs in Western societies, showing that the biomedical approach, and the monoamine hypothesis, still have a powerful influence on the treatment of depression. This is, in part at least, because many people see drugs as a 'quick fix' for depression and there is pressure to prescribe them (Section 1.5.3).

Evidence for the monoamine hypothesis

Serotonin is eventually broken down by enzymes and the breakdown products can be detected in the cerebrospinal fluid (CSF), which bathes the brain and spinal cord. Levels of serotonin breakdown products appear to be low in the CSF of people suffering from serious depression.

■ What do low levels of serotonin breakdown products suggest about levels of serotonin in the brain?

□ That levels of serotonin in the brain are low – the less there is, the less there is to break down.

Other evidence supporting the monoamine hypothesis comes from post-mortem studies of the brains of depressed people who committed suicide. Some studies have found abnormally high numbers of serotonin receptors in the prefrontal cortex in suicides (Stanley and Mann, 1983; Yates et al., 1990). The significance of increased numbers of serotonin receptors in the brain (or *up-regulation* of receptor numbers) is that it may enhance neurotransmission when serotonin levels are low, by facilitating the capture of as much of the available serotonin as possible.

■ What is the increase in numbers, or up-regulation, of serotonin receptors an example of?

□ It is an example of plasticity (Book 1, Section 2.2.2); in this case an adaptive change in the brain.

However, such effects are not always found in those who are depressed or have committed suicide. It has also become clear that not all those with depression respond to antidepressants such as SSRIs (as you will see in Chapter 3). One possibility is that the category of 'major depression' lumps together different kinds of depression (for instance early onset, late-onset and chronic or recurrent), which may differ in their biological bases. However, any such differences are not currently well understood, in part because they have not been well explored (see also Box 2.3).

Tryptophan depletion experiments

While the monoamine hypothesis still underlies the treatment of depression (Chapter 3), researchers now consider that, in its original form at least, it is too simplistic to explain the complex aetiology of depression.

The hypothesis postulates that low levels of monoamines cause depression, and as we have seen above, there appears to be some evidence for this. However, investigations into the link between monoamine levels and depression were typically carried out on people who were depressed at the time.

■ Why might this be a problem when studying, for instance, serotonin levels in depressed people?

□ Because cause cannot be distinguished from effect. Low serotonin levels in depressed people could be a *cause* of depression, but they could also be a *result* of depression. Or some unknown, third factor could underlie both depression and low serotonin levels.

Researchers have since tried to clarify the relationship between low monoamine levels and depression experimentally, by depleting the levels of monoamines in the brains of participants.

Serotonin is manufactured in the body from a chemical commonly found in the diet, the amino acid tryptophan. (Tryptophan is found in protein-rich foods, including meat, eggs, cheese and soybeans.)

Amino acids are the building blocks of proteins. Proteins are molecules that contribute to the structure and functioning of all our cells, including our neurons.

By feeding participants a special, otherwise well-balanced, diet free of tryptophan it is possible to reduce serotonin levels in their brains. The levels of the other monoamines, noradrenalin and dopamine, can also be depleted using similar techniques.

The findings of a meta-analysis by Ruhé et al. (2007) on the results of studies of monoamine depletion are summarised in Table 2.1. (You should be familiar with what a meta-analysis is from Box 1.7.) The groups listed in Table 2.1 are:

Group 1 – healthy participants who do not have, and have never had, major depression (MD), and have no family history of MD

Group 2 – Healthy participants who do not have, and have never had, MD, but do have a family history of MD

Group 3 – Patients in remission from MD who are not currently taking antidepressants

Group 4 – Patients in remission from MD who are currently taking antidepressants.

Table 2.1 Reaction to monoamine depletion.

	Participants			
	Group 1	**Group 2**	**Group 3**	**Group 4**
Depletion of tryptophan/ serotonin	No lowering of mood	Slightly lowered mood	Moderate decrease in mood	Induced relapse in those taking antidepressants that affect the serotonin system (such as SSRIs and SNRIs)
Depletion of noradrenalin/ dopamine levels	No lowering of mood	Slightly lowered mood	No lowering of mood	(No studies were available in this category)

■ Do any of these results suggest that lowering serotonin levels causes a lowering of mood or results in depression?

□ Patients in remission from MD who were taking antidepressants such as SSRIs and SNRIs that affect the serotonin system (Group 4) were likely to have a relapse if tryptophan/serotonin was depleted. Patients in remission from MD, but who were not currently taking antidepressants (Group 3) were also likely to experience low mood if serotonin was depleted. Participants (Group 2) who had a family history of depression showed slightly lowered mood. Thus lowering serotonin levels can have an effect on mood, albeit to different extents.

However, healthy participants without a personal or family history of major depression (Group 1) showed no mood changes, so serotonin depletion did not lower mood in everyone.

Overall, therefore, the results in Table 2.1 do not suggest a direct or consistent link between monoamine levels and major depression.

Booij et al. (2002), also analysing studies on tryptophan depletion, showed that (a) having had previous depressive episodes, (b) being female, (c) having had treatment with an SSRI, and (d) having a history of suicidal thoughts or attempts, were all strong predictors of whether tryptophan depletion (and hence serotonin depletion) would depress mood.

■ Consider Booij et al.'s suggestions above. Do any of them chime with any of the findings shown in Table 2.1?

□ Yes, (a) is consistent with the lowering of mood of patients in Group 3 and Group 4; (c) is consistent with the relapse of patients in Group 4.

One possibility is that a depressive episode changes the serotonin system in some way, making a person more vulnerable to the effects of future changes in serotonin levels.

A related possibility is that a subgroup of those with depression have a vulnerability or diathesis, due to their genetic make-up, that affects the workings of the serotonin system, making them particularly susceptible to depression when serotonin levels are depleted.

■ Is there any information in Table 2.1 which might fit in with this?

□ Yes – the finding that people in Group 2, who have not experienced major depression themselves but have a family history of depression, experience some lowering of mood following serotonin depletion.

To conclude, tryptophan-depletion experiments suggest that serotonin depletion has some effects on mood, but that there is no simple relationship between levels of monoamines and depression.

The next section considers an even more significant problem with the monoamine hypothesis, one that has fuelled much research and has led to a more sophisticated chemical and molecular hypothesis for the aetiology of depression.

2.3.2 The neurotrophic hypothesis of mood disorders

The most significant problem with the monoamine hypothesis in its original form is that, even though ADMs such as SSRIs raise the levels of serotonin in the brain almost immediately, it is many weeks before depressive symptoms are eased (Duman et al., 1997). Clearly, such a long delay is incompatible with the idea that monoamine levels *per se* are linked to mood.

What might be the reason for the delay? One influential idea is that processes such as the birth of neurons (or **neurogenesis**), or the growth or remodelling of connections between neurons, or changes to the number of receptors, which take time, are involved. All these are aspects of plasticity, which you met in Book 1, Section 2.2.2.

Neurotrophic means, literally, 'brain-feeding ' or 'brain-nurturing'.

If plasticity is involved, a class of brain chemicals called brain growth factors may play an important part. Such chemicals 'nurture' existing neurons and promote neurogenesis. **Brain-derived neurotrophic factor (BDNF)**, one of these brain growth factors, is known to operate in many areas of the brain, and significantly for our purposes, this includes the hippocampus and prefrontal cortex, which we already know are implicated in affective disorders.

Depression and levels of BDNF

As with monoamine levels, researchers have tried to establish whether there is a relationship between levels of BDNF and depression. BDNF levels in the blood of patients with major depression are abnormally low (Sen et al., 2008), and post-mortem studies show low levels of BDNF in the hippocampus and prefrontal cortex of depressed patients (Martinowich et al., 2007).

Such findings suggest that BDNF levels are correlated with mood, and have led to the **neurotrophic hypothesis of mood disorders**. In essence, the hypothesis states that 'reduced brain BDNF levels predispose to depression, whereas increases in brain BDNF levels produce an antidepressant action' (Duman and Monteggia, 2006). This may sound like a remarkably similar approach to that of the monoamine hypothesis, in that the *level* of a neurochemical, in this case BDNF, again seems the focus of a hypothesis to explain depression. Indeed the hypothesis has been criticised for this limited viewpoint on aetiology.

■ Which model of mental health is the neurotrophic hypothesis consistent with and why?

□ It is consistent with the biomedical model of mental health in focusing on the level of a particular chemical, BDNF. This carries the implication that correcting aberrant levels of BDNF will 'correct' mood disorders. It does not appear to acknowledge that psychosocial influences may play a part in the aetiology of mood disorders (and in treatments for them).

However, a major difference between the simple monoamine hypothesis and the neurotrophic hypothesis is that levels of BDNF have been linked to a complex series of processes involving the birth and death of neurons in some parts of the brain, and the experience of stress has been linked to such effects. Hence there is a strong potential for psychosocial factors to link into the neurotrophic model, as you will see below.

Stress, depression and neurogenesis in the hippocampus

Duman et al. (1997, 1999) suggested that the development of depression was likely to involve processes that affected plasticity. Several brain areas mentioned in Section 2.2.6, including the prefrontal cortex and hippocampus, are likely to be affected, but Duman and his colleagues focused their research on the hippocampus for a number of reasons. First, it had been discovered in the 1990s that, unusually for a structure in the adult human brain, the hippocampus continues to exhibit neurogenesis, making it a good candidate for the study of any changes in neurogenesis associated with depression or antidepressant treatment.

Second, there is evidence to suggest that neurogenesis in the hippocampus is highly susceptible to the effects of stress: especially when severe or prolonged, stress can inhibit neurogenesis and accelerate cell loss in the hippocampus. This effect appears to be due in large part to the effects of hormones such as cortisol (a glucocorticoid) that are overproduced by the adrenal gland during situations of chronic stress (Activity 2.1; Sapolsky (2000)).

Third, as we also considered in Section 2.2.2, there is evidence that stress and stressful events are important in triggering clinical depression (Kendler et al., 1999), and that depression in humans is associated with hyperactivity of the stress system.

Putting these pieces of the jigsaw together, current thinking is that stress, via the effects of glucocorticoid hormones, leads to a decline in hippocampal function (through some combination of decline in hippocampal neurogenesis and increase in hippocampal atrophy), and that hippocampal dysfunction is linked to some of the symptoms of depression.

■ Given what you know about the hippocampus from Activity 2.1, what kinds of symptoms of depression might be associated with hippocampal atrophy?

□ Impairments of some kinds of conscious memory, such as recollection of facts: the hippocampus plays a central part in memory processes supporting such memories.

Antidepressants, BDNF levels and neurogenesis in the hippocampus

If stress leads to a decline in neurogenesis, antidepressants seem to have exactly the opposite effect. There is now good evidence, from experimental work on rats, that ADMs such as Prozac®, an SSRI which increases levels of serotonin in the brain (Book 1, Section 2.4.1), stimulate the production of new neurons in the hippocampus (Malberg et al., 2000).

Importantly, Malberg et al. (2000), in experiments on rats, found that ADMs such as SSRIs only stimulate neurogenesis in the hippocampus if given every day for several weeks.

■ Why is this an important finding?

□ Because it fits well with, and has the potential to explain, the observation above that ADMs such as SSRIs show clinical efficacy only after several weeks of being given daily.

How does serotonin, levels of which are increased by SSRIs, have an effect on neurogenesis? It appears that serotonin stimulates the production of BDNF.

Why are BDNF levels low in the first place? Experimental evidence from animals suggests that stress (which, as you saw, releases powerful hormones such as glucocorticoids into the blood) reduces the levels of BDNF produced in the hippocampus, by damaging neurons in the hippocampus. This reduction in BDNF levels appears to be prevented or reversed by ADM treatment (Warner-Schmidt and Duman, 2006).

Indeed current evidence suggests that many antidepressant treatments, including SSRIs, **electroconvulsive therapy** (**ECT**, which you will read more about in Section 3.3.3), and exercise exert their effects by stimulating the production of BDNF in brain areas such as the hippocampus.

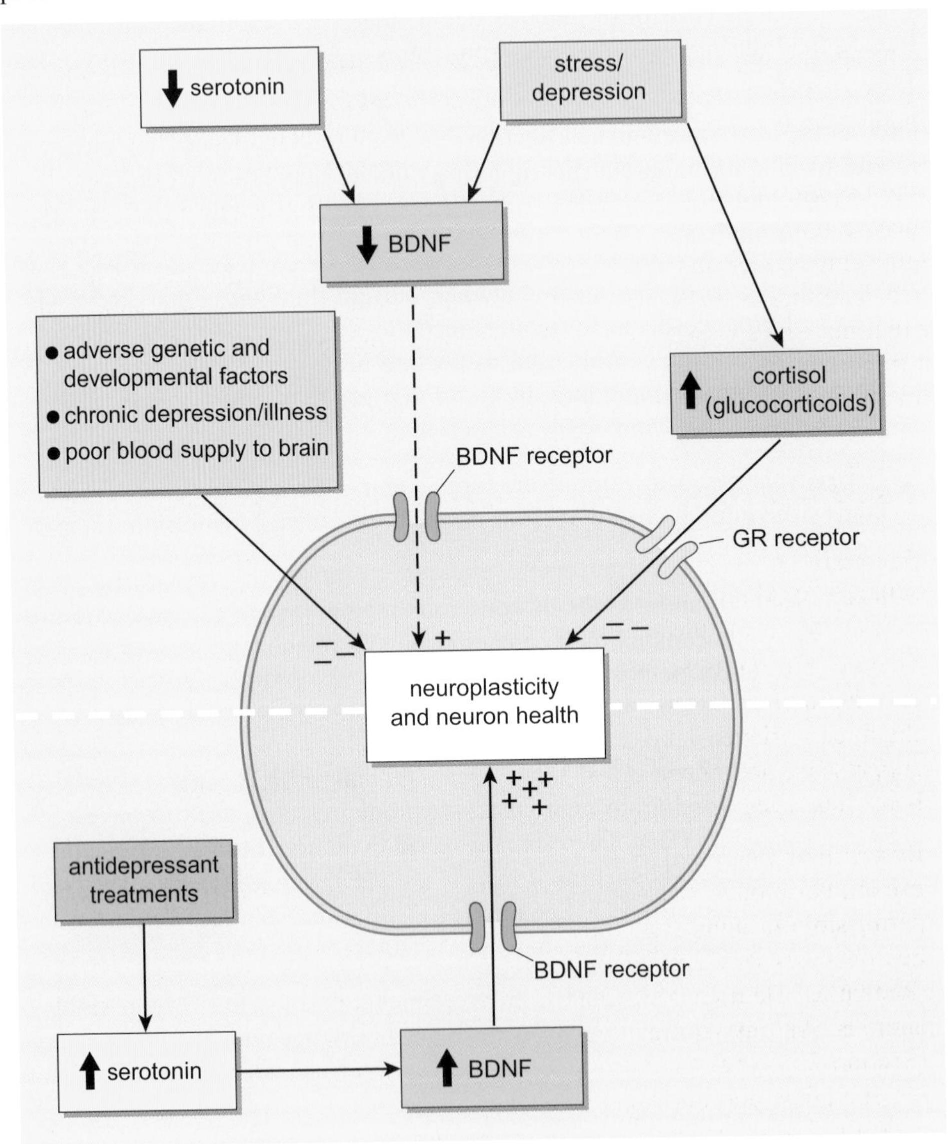

Figure 2.11 The neurotrophic hypothesis of mood disorders. The green area represents a neuronal cell. Within the cell is a box representing neuroplasticity and neuron health. Minus signs (−) indicate factors that damage neuroplasticity and neuron health, while plus signs (+) indicate factors that promote it. Some factors deleterious to neuroplasticity and neuron health are represented in the top half of the figure. For instance, low serotonin levels, and stress and depression, reduce the level of BDNF, weakening (as indicated by the broken line) its positive impact on neuroplasticity and neuron health; stress and depression also raise the level of cortisol, enhancing its negative impact on neuroplasticity and neuron health. The bottom half of the figure shows that antidepressant treatments, by raising levels of serotonin, and hence of BDNF, promote neuroplasticity and neuron health. BDNF: brain-derived neurotrophic factor; GR: glucocorticoid receptor. Up-arrows ↑ indicate an increase; down-arrows ↓ indicate a decrease.

Clearly, the neurotrophic hypothesis offers a much more complex and integrated view of the possible causes of depression, as shown in Figure 2.11. (The schema shown in Figure 2.11 also allows for the possibility that unknown genetic vulnerabilities could affect neuroplasticity and neuron health.)

To recap, the implication is that neurogenesis, promoted by ADMs via the release of BDNF, underlies the efficacy of ADMs. Thus a final question is whether there is any evidence for this. That is, are changes in behaviour consequent on taking ADMs linked to hippocampal neurogenesis? So far, this issue has only been addressed in a study in mice, but it appears that there is indeed a link. Santarelli et al. (2003) found that if neurogenesis in the mouse hippocampus was suppressed, ADMs failed to affect the behaviour of the mice. The results do not prove that a lack of neurogenesis causes depression, or that increased neurogenesis cures it, but it does suggest that neurogenesis is an important factor. Another important issue is that a mouse model does have limitations for understanding depression in humans (Box 2.4.)

Box 2.4 Animal models of depression and anxiety

Santarelli et al. (2003) used a standard mouse 'model' for testing the efficacy of ADMs. They placed hungry mice in an arena in which food was visible in the brightly lit centre. The more reluctant mice were to venture into the light to eat, the higher they scored on a scale of anxiety and depression. It was this behaviour that treatment with ADM affected: the mice retrieved food faster after ADM treatment. However, suppressing neurogenesis led to no improvements in food-retrieving behaviour even after ADM was taken.

Researchers interested in the neural bases of depression and anxiety often use animal models because the procedures needed would not be permissible in human studies. For instance, in Santorelli et al.'s study neurogenesis was suppressed using X-ray treatment to destroy cells (known as 'stem cells') in the mouse hippocampus that give birth to new neurons. And as you saw earlier, Mitra and Sapolsky (2008) (Section 2.2.6) used a rat model to assess the effects of corticosterone on the amygdala and on levels of anxiety. Anxiety level was assessed by measuring how long rats spent on the open arms of the elevated plus maze.

While animal models are unavoidable for some kinds of invasive, cutting-edge, research, the relevance of behavioural measures used in animal models to human experiences of depression and anxiety is an important question. It is also difficult to answer as we cannot find out about the cognitive and emotional experiences of animals directly. Moreover, while humans and animals such as rodents share a basic biological similarity there is no doubt that the human brain is far more complex, as are human social behaviour, cognition and emotions.

Given the likely limitations of animal models, definitive answers about the role of neurogenesis in depression may have to wait till scientists find better animal models, or find ways to look at neurogenesis directly in human patients. Meanwhile, attempts are being made to suggest why neurogenesis might be important, as a brief consideration of the final hypothesis in the next section shows.

2.3.3 The network hypothesis of mood disorders

While the neurotrophic hypothesis of mood disorders recognises the importance of BDNF and neurogenesis in explaining how antidepressants work, according to Eero Castre´n of the University of Helsinki, it does not go far enough in recognising the impact and significance of neurogenesis. He suggests that we need a conceptual framework to understand why neurogenesis might be important.

Castre´n (2005) quotes from the Nobel lecture given by Arvid Carlsson, the Swedish scientist who received the prize in 2000 in recognition of his work on the neurotransmitter dopamine: '…the brain is not a chemical factory but an extremely complicated survival machine'.

What does this mean? Castre´n argues that to understand how antidepressants work, and what their operation tells us about the brain bases of mood disorders, we need to look beyond the 'tools' – molecules such as BDNF – and try to understand what the tools are doing, which, he suggests, is repairing essential functional networks in the brain (Figure 2.12). A related point he makes is that there may be many different 'routes', including psychotherapy and ECT, that set in motion the plasticity processes needed to repair damaged networks (Figure 2.12c).

- ■ On this view, what is the significance of the results obtained by Santarelli et al. (2003) in the previous section, showing that antidepressants are ineffective if neurogenesis is suppressed?
- □ The results are significant because they suggest that neurogenesis is essential to the action of antidepressants. Castre´n suggests the new neurons are essential as they help 'repair' damaged networks in the brain, in this case in the mouse hippocampus, so the networks can function properly again.

One way of looking at the role of BDNF, then, is that it is not levels of BDNF as such that are important, or even that BDNF promotes neurogenesis. On the network hypothesis, BDNF's effects on behaviour will depend on *where* in the brain it is active, and which networks it therefore affects.

There is some evidence to support this view. While BDNF boosts neurogenesis in the hippocampus, and its actions there are 'antidepressant', Berton et al. (2006) found that in another area of the brain, the mesolimbic dopamine pathway, high levels of BDNF resulted in complete social withdrawal by mice who had been bullied by larger mice. In other words, the bullied mice, like subordinate animals (Section 1.3.5) behaved as if they were 'depressed'. This suggests that BDNF has very different effects on behaviour,

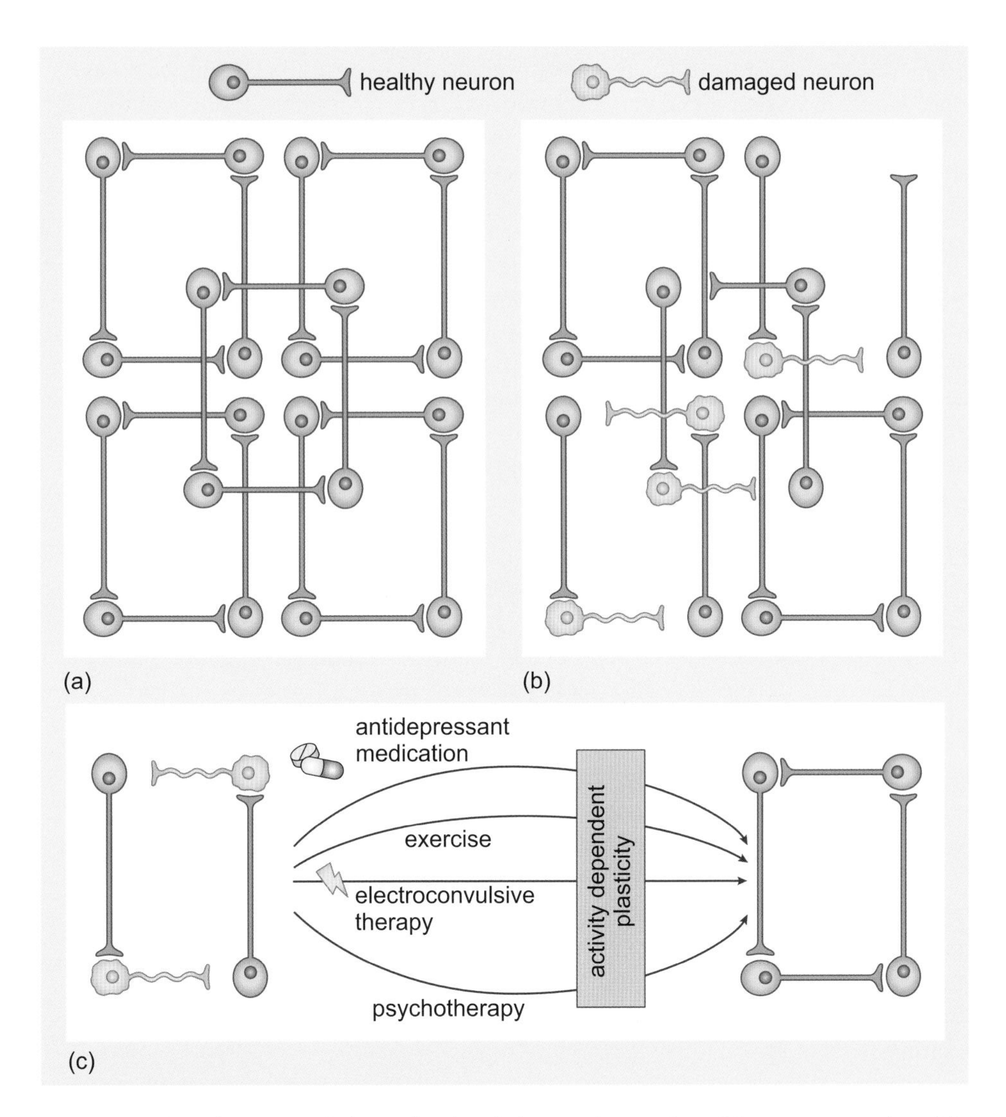

Figure 2.12 The network hypothesis of depression and antidepressant action (a) Networks of neurons process information in a healthy brain; (b) In depression, information processing networks do not function properly, as some neurons are damaged or have died; (c) Antidepressant treatment enhances connectivity in neuron networks: antidepressant medication, electroconvulsive therapy, exercise and psychotherapy can all enhance plasticity which gradually leads to the recovery of connections in damaged neuron networks.

depending on which part of the brain it is active in, and which circuits are being affected.

2.4 Genes and environment: bringing it all together

In Section 2.2.5 you saw that heritability values suggest that genetic and environmental factors both affect whether people develop mental disorders. Identical twins share the same genes, but if one identical twin develops schizophrenia, there is just a 50%–70% chance of the other one developing it too. This suggests a role for the environment in determining behaviour. On the other hand, it is also clear that experiences, or environment, alone cannot explain the aetiology of disorders. For instance, stressful or traumatic events can trigger clinical depression. But not all people who suffer such events become seriously depressed.

Thus, how an individual looks and behaves, including whether or not they have a mental disorder (their **phenotype**), is the product of an interaction between their inherited genetic make-up (their **genotype**) and environmental factors. Increasingly, psychologists are coming round to the idea, well-established amongst developmental biologists since the 1950s, that there is no question of it being 'nature versus nurture' – nature (our genotype) is in intimate interaction at all levels with nurture (our environment) to produce us (our phenotype) (See Box 2.5).

By environment we mean all the things outside our genes that can interact with them. This could be the environment of the cell in which the gene resides; it could be the environment in your mother's womb, where you could hear her heartbeat, and where chemicals from her blood passed into your blood. It could be the way in which you were treated as a baby, or the infections that you caught and the kind of food that you ate.

You might be wondering how such things could possibly interact with our genes, which are safely enclosed in the cells in our bodies. This is a very good question. In some cases, there is data to suggest that gene–environment interactions may be important, but it is not yet known how any effects are actually brought about. In other cases, an understanding of what may be happening in gene–environment interactions at the molecular level is beginning to emerge, though the picture is still far from complete. We consider some studies that are shedding light in this very important and exciting area in Box 2.5.

Box 2.5 Nature–nurture, diathesis–stress, gene–environment: what's the difference?

The short answer is that there is none. All these ideas or formulations address the same issue, the interaction between some kind of 'predisposition' – represented by nature, the diathesis (which is often seen as a pre-existing vulnerability), or a gene, and something outside the predisposition that interacts with it – represented, respectively, by nurture, a stressful environment or stressor, and the environment. Is it useful to have three different models of much the same thing? Quite possibly: the idea of nature–nurture is rather vague and bucolic, and while it might be good for arguments in the pub, it does not allow much precision in the discussion.

The greatest precision is allowed by the gene–environment model – there is no question here about what 'nature' might be. It is the activity of a gene. However, this precision itself could be a limitation in some respects, as becomes clearer when we consider the diathesis–stress formulation (Nemeroff, 1998). In essence this is a model that postulates interaction between biological factors and environmental factors. The term 'diathesis' is used to mean an inborn, genetic vulnerability or a predisposition to a particular disorder. The model assumes that exposure to a stressful environment can trigger behavioural disorder in an individual who is vulnerable, while individuals who are not vulnerable may experience similar stressors and not succumb. It allows some precision; however, it appears that the usage has evolved to allow changes in the phenotype – for instance, due to early animal handling or child abuse – to become diatheses themselves. Thus 'neuroticism' could be seen as a diathesis for the development of emotional disorders – although neuroticism itself may be a product of gene–environment interactions and hence a phenotype. As you will by now have realised, it is not easy to draw clear lines in this area!

2.4.1 The serotonin transporter gene and vulnerability to stressful life events

One approach that genetic epidemiologists initially took was to see if mood disorders such as depression could be linked to the kinds of genes people carry. (Genetic epidemiologists are epidemiologists who study the role of genetic factors and their interactions with environmental factors in the occurrence of diseases or disorders.)

As you have seen previously, serotonin (also known as 5-HT) has been the focus of much attention as a modulator of mood, and a lack of serotonin has been suggested as a factor in the development of depression. Indeed, selective serotonin reuptake inhibitors (SSRIs – Chapter 3; Book 1, Section 2.4.1) are widely used as ADMs. Thus a protein that is involved in serotonin reuptake, the serotonin transporter protein coded for by the *5-HTT* gene, has attracted much interest from genetic epidemiologists.

5-HT (5-hydroxytryptamine) is the chemical name for serotonin, so 5-HTT is the 'serotonin transporter': the second T stands for 'transporter'

Before going any further, it would be a good idea to read paragraph 1 in Box 2.6, to understand what genes are and how they work to produce proteins. (You do not need to read paragraphs 2 and 3 just yet; you will be directed to read these in a later section.)

Box 2.6 Genes, gene expression and epigenetic mechanisms

1 The human body contains around 100 trillion cells. Most cells contain an enclosed central area, the nucleus, which contains structures called chromosomes. In humans the nucleus typically contains 23 pairs of chromosomes. One chromosome in each pair is from the mother while the other is from the father. Each chromosome contains a long strand of DNA (short for deoxyribonucleic acid – you do not need to remember this!). The DNA contains the code for genes, written in chemical 'letters'. Genes are the templates for proteins – that is, they contain instructions for putting together protein molecules from

building blocks called amino acids. (You read about an amino acid, tryptophan, in Section 2.3.1.) Protein molecules are vital to life – they build and maintain our cells, including our neurons, and hence our brains and bodies.

2. To have an effect on the phenotype, a gene must actually be used to make the protein it codes for, a process called **gene expression**. A cell does not use every gene it contains to make a protein. Almost every cell in an individual contains the same genes, but different cells express different selections of genes. Such selective gene expression is what makes a muscle cell (for example) different from a neuron. The genes that are not expressed are said to be 'silenced'.
3. The main way to silence a gene is to physically block access to it so that the protein it codes for cannot be made. Methyl groups (a kind of chemical present in the body) are often used by cells to create such a barrier and block access to genes, a process called **methylation**. Access to a silenced gene can also be restored. Sometimes this can be done by removing the obstructing methyl groups (i.e. by **demethylation**). At other times it can be done by adding another chemical, acetyl groups, that facilitate greater access to genes. This process is known as **acetylation**. Such 'silencing' and 'de-silencing' mechanisms are examples of **epigenetic mechanisms**. The word 'epigenetic' means 'above or beyond genes' and is used to refer to the way the expression of genes can be altered as described above.

The *5-HTT* gene codes for the serotonin transporter protein – that is, it provides cells with the 'instructions' needed to make the protein. As a serotonin transporter, the protein is responsible for the reuptake of serotonin into the presynaptic cell after it has been released into the synaptic gap to signal to the adjacent neuron (Figure 2.9).

The number and activity of the serotonin transporters determines the length of time that serotonin will remain in the synaptic gap before reuptake into the presynaptic cell. The gene for the serotonin transporter comes in two variants, a short form (s) and a long form (l). Each person carries two copies, or **alleles**, of the gene, one from each parent. The 's' version produces less of the functional protein than the 'l' one.

■ As mentioned above, each individual carries two alleles, one allele ('s' or 'l') from the father and one ('s' or 'l') from the mother. What possible combination of alleles (or genotype) could an individual have?

□ The combinations are ss, ll or sl.

Genetic epidemiologists wondered if carrying one of the forms, 'l' or 's', made people more likely to develop depression. However, doing epidemiological studies (Book 1, Section 4.2.5) correlating the carrying of one or other of the *5-HTT* gene variants with the occurrence of depression failed to show a link.

Caspi et al. (2003) wondered if taking into account the level of stress people had experienced would clarify the picture. They determined which allele combinations were carried by each of the 847 participants in a long-term study (the New Zealand Dunedin study, which followed participants from birth), along with the number of major stresses they had experienced. When participants were 26 years old, the researchers evaluated how many stressful events they had experienced in the last 5 years, and whether or not they had depression. Caspi et al. (2003) found that people with either one or two short alleles (i.e. 'sl' or 'ss') were significantly more likely to develop depression following stress than people with two long alleles ('ll') (Figure 2.13a).

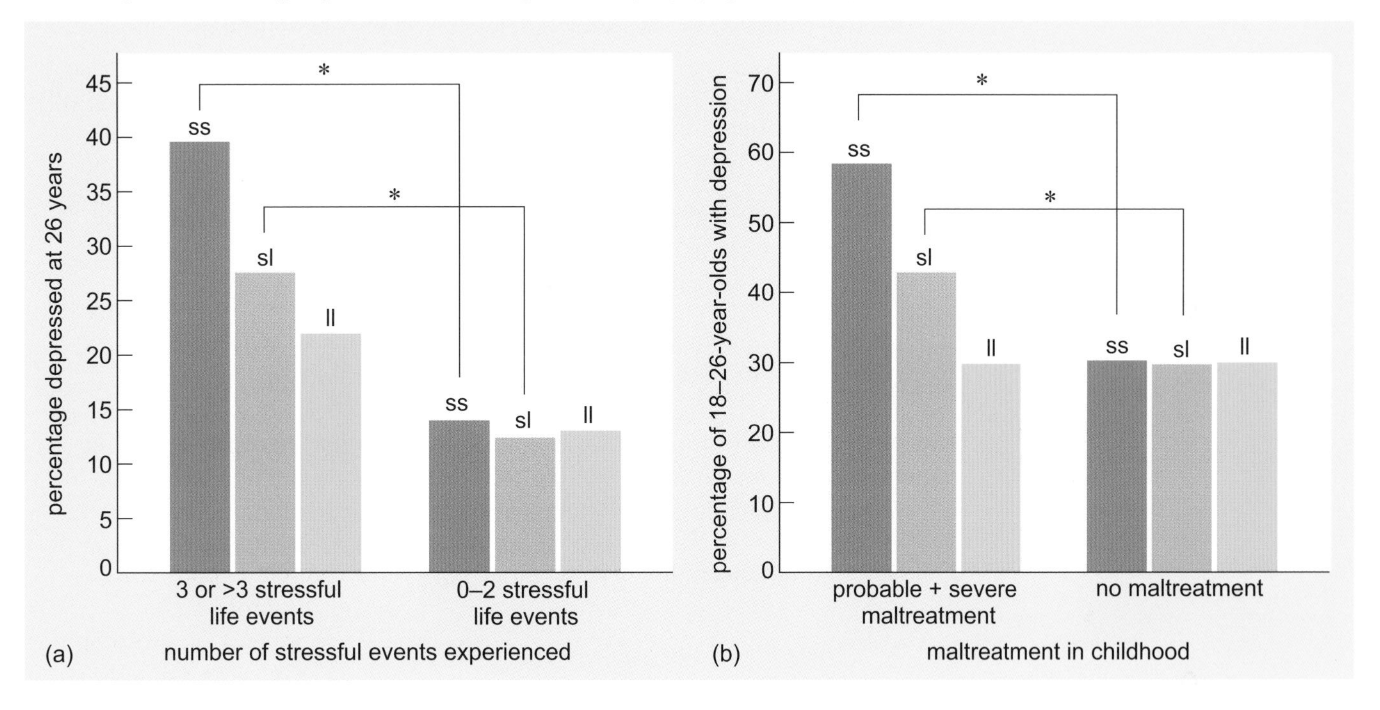

Figure 2.13 5-HTT genotype (ss, sl or ll), life stressors and the incidence of depression (a) Depression at age 26 years as a function of the number of stressful life events experienced between 21–26 years and 5-HTT genotype. Those with ss or sl genotypes who experienced 3 or >3 stressors were statistically significantly more likely to be depressed at 26 years than those with similar genotypes who had experienced only 0–2 stressors; (b) Depression between 18–26 years as a function of level of maltreatment in childhood and 5-HTT genotype. Those with ss or sl genotypes who experienced childhood maltreatment were statistically significantly more likely to be depressed between 18–26 years than those who were not maltreated in childhood. * denotes a statistically significant difference.

- ■ Did it matter how many stressful events participants had experienced in the last 5 years?
- □ Yes – 5-HTT genotype was associated with likelihood of depression only if three or more stressful events had occurred (Figure 2.13a).

Similarly, the researchers found that those who had experienced childhood maltreatment between 3 and 11 years were significantly more likely to be depressed between 18 and 26 years if they had the 'ss' or 'sl' genotype than if they had the 'll' genotype. There was no effect of 5-HTT genotype if maltreatment had not occurred (Figure 2.13b).

The importance of this study lies in its demonstration that genetic factors may not directly 'cause' disease, but may instead *mediate* responses to environmental factors such as stress (Caspi et al., 2003).

- ■ More than two-thirds of people apparently carry at least one short allele of the *5-HTT* gene. Does this mean they are all likely to get seriously depressed?
- □ No, carrying the 's' allele itself does not mean you are likely to get depressed. What it does mean is that the chances of getting depressed may be higher compared to people who have two long alleles ('ll'), if a person with two or one short alleles has many stressful experiences.

While an effect of carrying these combinations might exist (though the results of studies to replicate this finding are mixed to date – Risch et al., 2009; Hammen et al., 2010), it is not known how the effects might come about.

- ■ The 's' allele of the *5-HTT* gene causes decreased production of the functional protein – that is, fewer serotonin transporters are produced. What might happen if fewer serotonin transporters are available?
- □ The rate of reuptake of serotonin might be reduced, since these transporters are involved in reuptake of serotonin.

However, successful treatment of depression has often involved serotonin reuptake inhibitors, so it is puzzling that decreased production of the transporter responsible for this reuptake seems to exacerbate depression. It is evident that much is still unclear about precisely how serotonin or serotonin reuptake inhibitors might act to affect mood.

2.4.2 Genes, environment and development

Caspi et al.'s (2003) results suggest how gene–environment interactions (sometimes written as GxE interactions) might help explain the incidence of some disorders such as major depression, though the precise mechanisms involved (i.e. exactly how the two interact) are not known. However, understanding of genetics has recently undergone a profound paradigm shift in the light of evidence that the environment can affect the working of genes in ways that were thought impossible in the recent past.

Epigenetic mechanisms

To have an effect on the human phenotype a gene must be used to make a protein, a process known as gene expression (paragraph 2, Box 2.6). Scientists have recently shown that gene expression can in effect be switched on and off through epigenetic mechanisms (paragraph 3, Box 2.6).

Many common environmental factors or experiences are now known to trigger epigenetic mechanisms, including diet and exercise.

It is important to note that the genes themselves (that is, the DNA, and the codes it provides for making proteins) are not changed by the action of epigenetic mechanisms – the genes remain exactly the same.

What is it that changes, then, when epigenetic changes occur? Think of a factory with lots of machinery for manufacturing different kinds of chocolate.

If one of the machines is switched off, then that kind of chocolate is no longer produced. The machine is still there, unchanged, and it has not lost the capacity to make this particular chocolate, but it cannot make the chocolate because it is switched off. In this analogy, the machine is the equivalent of the gene or the genetic code for making a particular protein, and the epigenetic change is the equivalent of the switch – it can switch genetic machinery for making particular proteins on, or off.

Epigenetic effects and anxiety

What can epigenetics add to our understanding of mental disorders? To answer this question we need to go back to some pioneering animal studies conducted over 50 years ago by Seymour Levine (Levine, 1957). He showed that rat pups that were briefly separated from their mother were less anxious as adults. These effects persisted into old age and seemed to be caused by the extra maternal care that the pups received on return to the mother, which included a great deal of maternal licking and grooming.

The extra care appeared to be elicited by distress calls made by the rat pups following separation.

The offspring of high-licking, high-grooming mothers showed less stress-system activity, improved cognitive performance in tests of learning, and reduced anxiety-like behaviour in adulthood. This kind of long-term effect of early experience is an example of a programming effect (see Section 2.2.7 and Box 2.7).

In a later study Michael Meaney and his team at McGill University (Meaney, 2001) compared the stress response of rats whose mothers had vigorously licked and groomed them during the first 10 days of their lives, with that of rats whose mothers rarely licked and groomed them as pups. They found that the offspring of high lickers and groomers displayed less anxiety and stress than the pups of low lickers and groomers when they were confined to a small plastic tube for 20 minutes. Levels of the rat stress hormone, corticosterone (a glucocorticoid) shot up higher and stayed high for longer in the rats that had low-licking and low-grooming mothers than they did in the rats whose mothers had been high lickers and groomers.

■ Can we be certain that the effects on rat pups observed by Meaney and his co-workers were due to the mothers' behaviour? Explain your reasoning.

□ No, we can't. The rat pups share genes with their mothers, so it could be that the pups of calm, stress-resistant high-licking, high-grooming mothers were genetically different from the pups of anxious, emotionally reactive, low-licking, low-grooming mothers. So it is possible that the behaviours seen in the pups were mediated by genes inherited from their mothers, rather than by the way their mothers treated them.

Meaney and his colleagues were able to do an elegant experiment to show that it was indeed the maternal licking and grooming behaviour that made the difference. They placed the offspring of anxious, emotionally reactive mothers with calm, stress-resistant mothers, who frequently licked and groomed their adopted pups. Conversely, the pups of calm, stress-resistant mothers were placed with anxious mothers, who not surprisingly rarely licked and groomed them. When the offspring reached maturity, their behaviour, including reactivity to stress, resembled the behaviour of their adoptive mothers rather than that of their biological mothers (Meaney, 2001; Figure 2.14).

Box 2.7 When anxious or socially avoidant behaviour can be an advantage

The studies of Meaney and his colleagues (Meaney, 2001) confirm that early life events that increase stress reactivity can result in a greater vulnerability to stress over a long period – in other words, stressful early experiences can have 'programming' effects (Section 2.2.7) that affect an animal for life. So it may be tempting to think that rat pups with high-nurturing mothers get a better deal in life than rat pups with low-nurturing mothers.

However, it would be a mistake to think this – it all depends on the context. Rats living in a laboratory or other safe environment, with plenty of food and shelter, can afford to be relaxed. Rats in the wild are likely to live in environments with less food and more predators, so a mother may well not be available when her pups are distressed, or she may be anxious and stressed herself and less likely to be nurturing. In a dangerous environment her 'less-nurturing' maternal behaviour would quickly 'programme' her pups to keep a low profile and be highly responsive to stressors, in other words to behave more anxiously. This could well save their lives if there were many predators around. In such an environment a relaxed pup would be the one at a disadvantage.

Similarly, a socially avoidant mouse, like the small mouse in Nestler's study (Tsankova et al., 2006) may, in the same way as a subordinate monkey (Section 1.3.5), be pursuing the best strategy for survival in an environment where larger and more aggressive animals are around as competitors.

But how exactly could maternal nurturing behaviour – or the lack of it – shape the rat pups' physiological reaction to stress? Meaney and his colleagues suspected that the answer might lie in how glucocorticoids such as corticosterone act to calm the stress response during normal working of the HPA axis (See Activity 2.1).

■ How do glucocorticoids calm the response of the HPA axis during its normal operation?

□ Glucocorticoids (like corticosterone), released during the stress response, bind to GRs on brain structures such as the hippocampus and hypothalamus, with the end result that the hypothalamus is inhibited from producing CRF. This calms the activity of the HPA axis and reduces the production of stress hormones such as corticosterone (or cortisol in humans) (Activity 2.1).

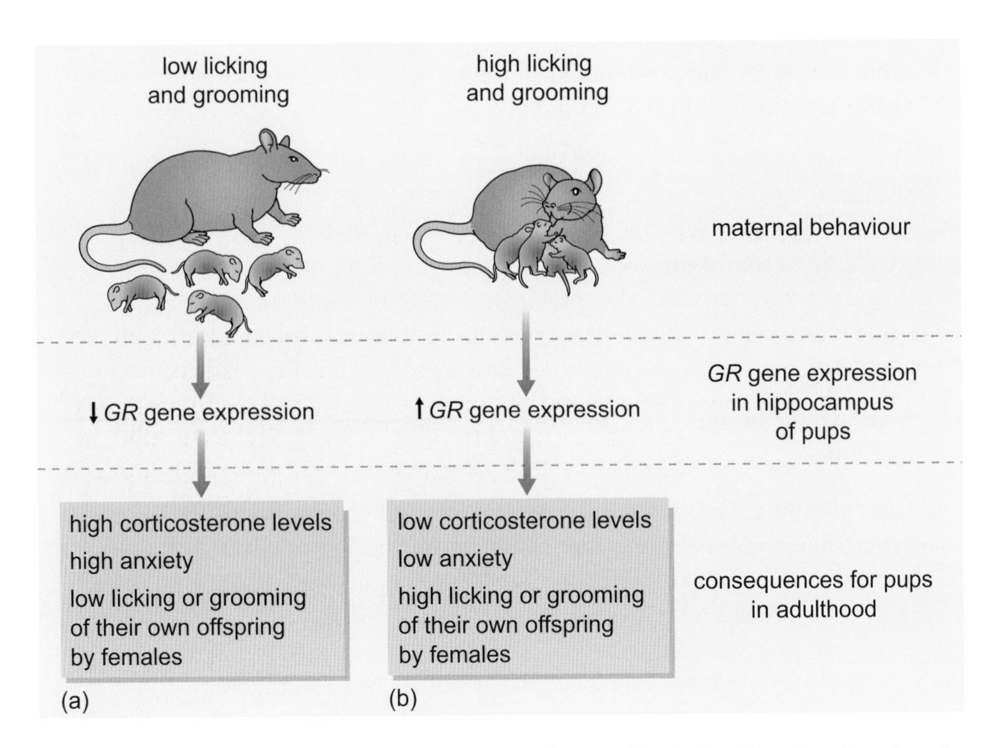

Figure 2.14 'Licky' and 'non-licky' rat mothers with their offspring showing the effects of these behaviours on glucocorticoid receptor (*GR*) gene expression and stress responsiveness. (a) Receiving low licking and grooming results in low levels of *GR* gene expression in the hippocampus. Low levels of *GR* gene expression are linked to high anxiety and high levels of corticosterone in adulthood. Female pups with low-licking and low-grooming mothers become low-licking and low-grooming mothers themselves. (b) Receiving high licking and grooming results in high levels of *GR* gene expression in the hippocampus. High levels of *GR* gene expression are linked to low anxiety and low levels of corticosterone in adulthood. Female pups with high-licking and high-grooming mothers become high-licking and high-grooming mothers themselves.

Glucocorticoid receptors are proteins, and like all proteins, are created by gene expression (Box 2.6). Meaney and his team (Weaver et al., 2004) were able to show that the effect of early experience was mediated by an effect on the gene expression of the glucocorticoid receptor gene (or *GR* gene). The *GR* gene is heavily methylated and thus silenced in newborn rat pups, and it is maternal behaviour that determines if the gene remains silent or not. Rats that receive a lot of maternal care (licking and grooming) as pups express the *GR* gene and grow more glucocorticoid receptors in their hippocampus; they consequently have less CRF produced by their hypothalamus, and show reduced anxiety and fear as adults.

The glucocorticoid receptor gene is more likely to remain 'silenced' in the pups with mothers who lick and groom them less.

Meaney and his co-workers then decided to see whether they could reverse this silencing – in other words, whether they could make the gene available again – in the rats with less 'caring' mothers.

It is worth mentioning that the glucocorticoid receptor gene is just one of hundreds of genes known to be affected by maternal licking and grooming behaviour.

- ■ What would be the consequences of 'de-silencing', or switching on the glucocorticoid receptor gene again?
- □ The gene could be expressed, so more glucocorticoid receptors would be produced.

Weaver, Meaney and their colleagues administered a compound thought to 'de-silence' the glucorticoid receptor genes so they could be accessed and more glucocorticoid receptors produced in the hippocampus and hypothalamus.

- ■ What would be the consequences of producing more glucocorticoid receptors?
- □ The calming effect exerted via glucocorticoid receptors on the hypothalamus, and by the hippocampus on the hypothalamus, would become effective again. Hence the stress response mediated by the HPA axis could be controlled better.

The extraordinary (but not unexpected!) result of this treatment was that it cancelled out the effect of the anxious rats' less 'salubrious' upbringing. The treated rats were no longer as anxious when they were trapped in the tube, and their stress hormone levels became similar to those of rats raised by high-licking and high-grooming mothers.

Weaver et al. (2004) clearly used the equivalent of a drug treatment on their rats to reverse the effects of their upbringing. However, experiential factors can also act to reverse deprivation or to compensate for it. Thus when rat pups with low levels of maternal care were provided with an enriched and stimulating environment, the hippocampal and cognitive differences between them and pups who received high levels of maternal care disappeared (Bredy et al., 2004). This finding may remind you of the neurotrophic and network hypotheses we considered in Sections 2.3.2 and 2.3.3, which suggest how repair of neural networks could happen via different pathways.

To conclude this section it is worth mentioning that at the time of writing, research by the McGill researchers suggests that expression of the *GR* gene is possibly also implicated in human mental disorders (see Box 2.8).

Box 2.8 Epigenetic effects and human mental disorders

Animal models have helped to elucidate how social experience, via epigenetic mechanisms, 'translates' into effects on the expression of genes, and hence into long-lasting effects on behaviour.

Such investigations have paved the way for the study of epigenetic effects in human mental disorders. The McGill group that discovered that rat maternal behaviour affects expression of the *GR* gene in the hippocampus of rat pups, recently investigated whether early adverse experience is linked to epigenetic modification of the *GR* gene in humans. McGowan et al. (2009) looked at post-mortem hippocampal tissue from humans, comparing three groups: (i) suicide victims with a history of child abuse; (ii) suicide victims without a history of child abuse, and (iii) non-suicide controls, people with no history of child abuse who had died suddenly.

They found that *GR* gene expression in the hippocampus of abused suicide victims was lower than in the hippocampus of non-abused suicide victims or controls. As in rat pups, the epigenetic mechanism silencing *GR* gene expression was methylation (Box 2.6). McGowan and his colleagues found higher levels of *GR* gene methylation in abused suicide victims than in non-abused suicide victims or in controls.

The effects of epigenetic modification in humans (and in animals) are undoubtedly hugely complex, as a great many genes besides the *GR* gene are known to be epigenetically modified by experiential factors. However, McGowan et al.'s findings suggest that epigenetic mechanisms of the kind known to be important in animals could also be implicated in the long-term effects of adverse early experience on mental health in humans.

Epigenetic effects and depression

Another experiment, by Eric Nestler and his colleagues, suggests that epigenetic modification may play a role in the development of depression. Knowing that depression can follow stressful experiences, and the link postulated between depression and BDNF (Section 2.3.2), Nestler and his colleagues hypothesised that distressing experiences might act on the gene that codes for BDNF.

Nestler and his colleagues (Tsankova et al., 2006) induced helplessness (a state that somewhat resembles depression) in mice. They did this by putting a small adult male mouse into the cage of a larger aggressive ('bully') mouse (Figure 2.15), which soon attacked the newcomer and defeated it. Ten minutes later they placed a plastic barrier between the mice, which stopped the attacks but did not stop the small defeated mouse from seeing, hearing and smelling the aggressor. Each small mouse was exposed to a different bully mouse every day for 10 days. The controls were small mice who were not exposed to bully mice, but to other small mice, and hence did not experience defeat.

At the end of the treatment, all mice were tested for socially avoidant behaviour by recording the percentage of time they spent in an 'interaction zone' around a cage placed in an arena. When the cage was empty, both control and defeated mice spent a similar percentage of time in the 'interaction zone'. However, when a 'bully' mouse was in the cage, control mice spent more time in the interaction zone, showing interest in the bully mouse, while defeated mice spent much less time in the interaction zone, avoiding social interaction.

In this 'social defeat stress' animal model, such social avoidance was used as a measure of helplessness, defeat and 'depression' (see also Box 2.4).

Nestler and his colleagues found that treating defeated mice with ADMs such as imipramine or fluoxetine (an SSRI: Prozac®) every day for a month reversed social avoidance – that is, treated defeated mice and control mice spent similar amounts of time in the interaction zone when a bully mouse was in the cage. (Treating control mice with ADMs did not have any effect on their behaviour.)

Figure 2.15 Small mouse and larger (so-called 'bully') mouse.

The defeated mice were found to have abnormally low levels of BDNF in their brains, especially in the hippocampus. Examination of the *BDNF* gene in the bullied mice showed that it had a high level of methylation compared to that in control mice.

■ What effect would methylation of the *BDNF* gene have on the production of BDNF?

□ Methylation (Box 2.6) would silence the *BDNF* gene, so it could not be used as a template for production of BDNF.

So it seems that the threatening experiences had silenced the *BDNF* gene. Nestler and his colleagues found that treating the defeated mice with ADM every day for a month (which, as you saw above reversed their socially avoidant 'depressive' behaviour), boosted production of BDNF – apparently by adding acetyl groups (see paragraph 3, Box 2.6).

■ What would be the effect on access to the *BDNF* gene of adding acetyl groups, or 'acetylation'?

□ The *BDNF* gene would be 'de-silenced': access to it would be restored, so it could be expressed again, and BDNF would be produced.

Interestingly, other depression treatments may have a similar effect on the *BDNF* gene. For example, in a previous study Nestler's team found that ECT, when applied to depressed rodents, also increased access to the *BDNF* gene via acetylation. The researchers speculated that psychotherapy might have the same effect – but of course this is something that cannot be tested on a mouse model!

2.5 Final word

A major aim of this chapter was to shed some light on the aetiology of depression and anxiety. At the end of this chapter you should have some idea of the complexity of this enterprise. We have focused on one of the best-studied and hence best-understood contributors to psychopathology – stress. This has biological, social and psychological significance, and its operation can be studied and understood at all these levels.

The clear message you should take away from this chapter is that interaction between these levels is enormously important in aetiology. Biological factors, such as dysregulation of the HPA axis and its consequences, possible abnormalities in brain neurotransmitter systems, the effects of stress on the developing brain at different ages, and the kinds of genes that an individual carries, appear to play an important part in the development and maintenance of emotional disorders such as depression and anxiety. However, these biological factors cannot be divorced from factors that are thought of as psychosocial, such as nurturing or abuse in childhood, or stressful events and how we perceive them. This is very evident from the most recent developments in genetics, which show how, via epigenetic processes, experiences are translated into the activity (or expression) of genes, which then modify the workings of the brain in ways that affect mood.

Research into epigenetic influences on mental health and ill-health is burgeoning and is likely to make a very significant contribution to our understanding of aetiology in the years to come. If so, it should also help clarify how existing treatments, both pharmacological and psychotherapeutic, for emotional disorders work, or suggest new approaches that would work more effectively.

Current approaches to treatment are considered in the next chapter.

2.6 Summary of Chapter 2

- The HPA axis is overactive in those with depression and anxiety, suggesting a role for chronic stress. Elevated levels of glucocorticoids such as cortisol and corticosterone, resulting from chronic stress, have toxic effects in some areas of the brain and promote neuron growth in others.
- The monoamine hypothesis of mood disorders has been influential in trying to explain the causes of depression. However the picture is now more complex and the view of a simple chemical imbalance as a cause of depression is outdated.
- Hypotheses such as the neurotrophic hypothesis and the network hypothesis have been developed to try to account for the complex effects of antidepressant treatments on the brain.
- The life-cycle model of stress links brain development with stress effects over the lifetime.
- The cognitive approach concentrates on particular ways of thinking and how these cause and sustain depression.
- Genetic and other vulnerabilities (also called predispositions or diatheses) can interact with environmental factors, which include psychosocial stressors such as stressful life events and early life stress (including child abuse) to cause emotional disorders such as depression.
- Epigenetic processes add another layer of complexity to the interaction between genes and environment. There is increasing evidence of the importance of epigenetic processes in the aetiology of mood disorders.

2.7 Learning outcomes

LO 2.1 Describe how stressful life events may be linked to the aetiology or maintenance of emotional disorders such as depression and anxiety. (CS1)

LO 2.2 Describe the main features of the physiological stress response, including the working of the hypothalamic–pituitary–adrenal axis (HPA axis), and explain how stress affects the brain. (KU2, KU4, CS1)

LO 2.3 Evaluate the role of genetic and environmental factors in the aetiology of emotional disorders. (KU1, KU2, KU3, KU5, CS3, CS4, CS5)

LO 2.4 Describe the different kinds of biological abnormalities that have been linked to emotional disorders, and the nature of their effect(s). (KU2, CS4)

LO 2.5 Evaluate the evidence for and against different hypotheses that aim to explain the causes and treatment of depression and anxiety. (KU1, KU2, KU3, KU5, CS3, CS4, CS5)

2.8 Self-assessment questions

SAQ 2.1 (LO 2.1)

Is there any truth in the assertion that 'How you think affects how stressed you feel'?

SAQ 2.2 (LO 2.2)

Where is cortisol produced, and on which part(s) of the HPA (hypothalamic–pituitary–adrenal) axis does it have an inhibitory effect?

SAQ 2.3 (LO 2.3)

On balance, does the evidence suggest that emotional disorders such as depression and anxiety are caused by genetic factors or by factors in the environment?

SAQ 2.4 (LO 2.4)

Name the main neurotransmitters implicated in the monoamine hypothesis of mood disorders. Are the levels of these neurotransmitters higher or lower in people who are depressed?

SAQ 2.5 (LO 2.5)

It takes many weeks of taking antidepressants such as SSRIs to improve mood. Why is this a problem for the monoamine hypothesis as it was originally conceived?

Chapter 3 Treating emotional disorders

Heather McLannahan

3.1 Introduction

All of the conditions discussed in the previous two chapters can range from being experienced as a very slightly altered state of mood, being only mildly different from 'normal' mood changes, to being a state of existence that overwhelms all other aspects of day-to-day life – a condition so severe and overwhelming that it becomes impossible to live a normal life. At this point, if not before, most people will seek help – or it may be that someone else will seek help on their behalf.

In this chapter we will look at a range of therapies being used by the UK National Health Service (NHS) for some emotional disorders: from the traditional biomedical approach of prescription drugs to psychological and behaviour therapies. There is not enough space to consider counselling and other psychotherapies, most of which are only available to those who can afford to purchase them. The relative efficacy of the different approaches will be assessed as well as the extent to which these different treatments and their outcomes can be related to the biological and psychological theories of the mechanisms that underlie these conditions, some of which have been discussed in the previous chapter.

Activity 3.1 Scene setting

(LOs 3.1, 3.2 and 3.4) Allow 45 minutes

Now would be an ideal time to go to the multimedia map and listen to the interviews with a number of therapists and those who have received treatment for emotional disorders. Then follow the instructions in the activity.

One thing that should have struck you as you listened to these interviews was the variety of experiences and opinions expressed. There is no 'one size fits all' when it comes to the experience of, or the treatments for, mental ill-health.

3.2 Coping with depression

Book 1 showed how a biopsychosocial model could help you to understand Neha's story. Her social situation was unenviable – a 'traumatic divorce' and death of parents, 'now on her own' having come from 'a close-knit community and extended family'. This situation would be likely to depress even someone with the most optimistic explanatory style (Book 1, Section 3.5.3). When you first met Neha (Book 1, Section 1.1.1), the therapist was working to persuade her that she had to challenge her negative belief that she was a failure at everything. You were told that Neha was taking Prozac®, a selective serotonin reuptake inhibitor (SSRI). For many people who take Prozac®, this biological manipulation has a beneficial psychological effect and eventually they are able to view their situation less negatively (Book 1, Section 2.4.1). In Neha's case she was eventually able to take decisive action to alter her social situation and to return to live near members of her extended family within their supportive, close-knit community.

Neha's depression had developed as a gradual process. Like most of us, her losses (parents, partner and community) caused her to experience a time of sadness and morbid introspection. But as time passed she didn't manage to rid herself of these feelings; quite the reverse, the negative feelings strengthened and deepened, overwhelming her, despite her best efforts. Neha tried to cheer herself up in a number of ways.

1 She played cheerful music but found that it irritated her.
2 She accepted invitations from colleagues to go out for a drink after work but she felt she was a boring person; sitting with them but not knowing what to say.
3 She went to the cinema with a friend but all the negative characteristics of the major protagonists seemed to be a mirror of all her failings.
4 She went shopping for some new clothes but thought that everything she tried on looked ugly on her.
5 She phoned her sister but everything her sister said seemed to be a criticism of Neha.

It is believed that many people are mildly depressed for long periods of time and struggle along trying to find ways to cheer themselves up. Often it works; having a can of beer whilst watching a TV sports channel works wonders if your team wins. For many people the cost of the sports channel may be too high for them to subscribe, but, strangely, that might work in their favour if they live near enough to a pub or club that does have that facility. The social atmosphere of watching with others can in itself increase positive affect. However, the drink of beer isn't such a good idea. Although popular opinion may suggest that a glass or two of something alcoholic will improve mood, alcohol is in fact a sedative.

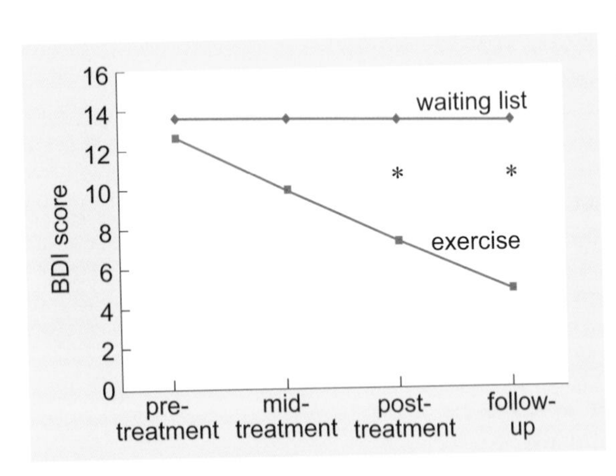

Figure 3.1 A comparison of the effects of exercise and a control condition ('waiting list') on mood, using the Beck Depression Inventory (BDI). The BDI was administered before treatment, one week later (mid-treatment), one week after the intervention had been completed (post-treatment) and the follow-up was after another 3 weeks. * denotes a statistically significant difference between the BDI scores of those on the waiting list and those in the exercise group (for example, at post-treatment).

Jogging along the street with motivating music on your iPod is another excellent 'pick-me-up' because physical exercise can alter psychological states. We will now consider in detail the part of the experiment quoted in Book 1, Section 3.3 that gave grounds for this conclusion. In that section, you saw the results for an experiment where a group of participants who had taken part in an exercise programme were compared to a group who were on a waiting list for the exercise programme. Figure 3.1 shows how their mood (as measured by the Beck Depression Inventory (BDI) – see Book 1, Box 4.9) changed over time.

This was a carefully conducted experiment and you should read Box 3.1 to find out the issues that have to be considered when designing such an experiment.

Box 3.1 Research Methods: Validity and reliability

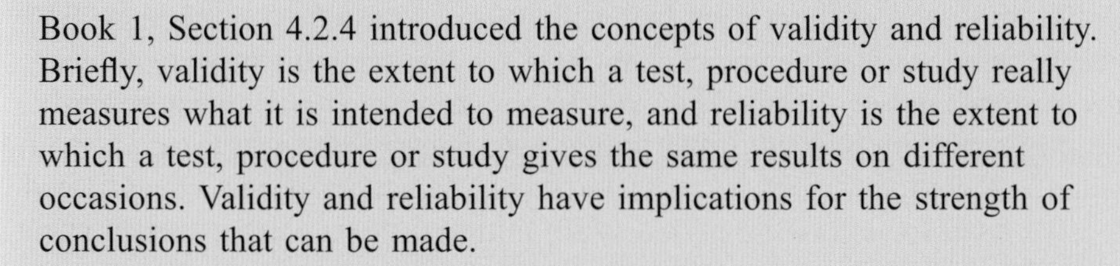

Book 1, Section 4.2.4 introduced the concepts of validity and reliability. Briefly, validity is the extent to which a test, procedure or study really measures what it is intended to measure, and reliability is the extent to which a test, procedure or study gives the same results on different occasions. Validity and reliability have implications for the strength of conclusions that can be made.

In particular, the concepts of validity and reliability can be applied to experimental studies such as the one described in Section 3.2 which investigated the effect of an exercise programme on mood. There are two aspects of validity that are important to consider when designing an experiment:

The first is **internal validity** which relates to how well the experiment is designed and conducted. Internal validity is only truly achieved if all variables that could influence the outcome of the study other than the one being manipulated by the researcher (in this case exercise) have been controlled. For example, to have internal validity there should be no confounding variables (see Box 2.2). However, in an experiment that involves people who are for the rest of the time going about their everyday business and come with different backgrounds and histories, it is almost impossible to achieve internal validity. In this case assigning participants randomly to the exercise and the control groups would be an essential and helpful procedure.

It is also important to avoid the possibility of bias affecting the results: for example, a researcher might inadvertently measure the dependent variable differently in one group of participants due to different expectations about their performance. Therefore, if possible, it is better to use someone who is not involved in the research programme and does not know the reason for taking the measurements. Additionally, using a self-assessment test will go some way towards overcoming this problem.

The second aspect is **external validity** which is a measure of how relevant the results are to other people and situations beyond the experimental setting. For example, can the results of the exercise study be applied to a wider population than the 60 people, mainly psychology students, who were recruited for the study? Does the structured, supervised exercise programme have any relevance to a real-life situation in which people might engage with moderate exercise in order to lift their mood?

The experimenters addressed the issue of reliability by using a tried and tested technique (the BDI) which provides a quantitative measure of mood. Applying a statistical test to the results introduces another level of reliability (this will be explored further in Book 4).

The 60 participants in this study were mostly first-year psychology students who were experiencing symptoms of anxiety. None of them took regular exercise and none of them were being given any form of psychotherapy. The students were awarded partial course credit for completing the programme; other participants were paid. The exercise programme was administered to each participant individually by a trainer who ensured that the exercise, on a treadmill, was of sufficient intensity to raise their heart rate to a consistently intensive level for a training period of 20 minutes, three times a week.

The whole exercise programme only lasted 2 weeks and there does not appear to have been any attempt to discover whether the participants might have continued to engage in similar moderately intensive exercise after the supervised intervention. Although the researchers were interested in whether the exercise would reduce anxiety, they also looked at other aspects of affect. For example, the extent to which each participant could be described as depressed was assessed using the BDI where the maximum score that could be obtained is 63 (Book 1, Box 4.9).

■ Using the values given in Book 1, Section 4.3.3, does Figure 3.1 suggest that these people were depressed?

□ On average, none of the participants was more than minimally depressed. (A score of 0–13 indicates minimal depression.)

■ Using Figure 3.1, what evidence is there that the exercise was beneficial?

□ The groups that engaged in physical exercise showed an immediate improvement in mood whilst exercising, and their mood continued to improve after the treatment was over.

The results from this study endorse the idea that taking exercise can help to lift one out of a low mood. It would seem to be a good coping strategy. But it should be pointed out that although these participants had all volunteered to take part in this programme, there was still a 25% drop-out from the treatment group. It may be that the 'drop-outs' found the exercise regime too tough or they might have felt uncomfortable with some of the questions they were asked; the authors of the paper do not say. But it is well known in the health services that recovery is best aided by the patients themselves wishing to be involved. Occupational therapists, in particular, concern themselves with working with their patient's **volition**; their own freely chosen desire to participate in the selected treatment. And herein lies a problem in suggesting that exercise is a good antidote to mild depression: depressed individuals may not wish to participate. It is observed that in the population in general, those who take regular exercise experience fewer depressive symptoms. De Moor and colleagues (2008) used a longitudinal study (1991–2002) to find out whether this was cause and effect.

A longitudinal study takes records from the same people over an extended period of time (Book 1, Box 4.5).

They were able to use information from over 8000 individuals registered at the Netherlands Twin Register and their analysis confirmed that those who exercise the most experience the least depression. But they found that this was not a causal relationship; rather, it is explained by underlying genetic factors. Those genetically predisposed to take more exercise are also predisposed to experience less depression and vice versa. So someone inclined to depression is also inclined to not engage in exercise. That doesn't mean that exercise wouldn't do them any good; it just means that left to themselves, this isn't likely to be their choice of a coping strategy.

Activity 3.2 What do you do to 'beat the blues'?

(LO 3.1) Allow 10 minutes – more if you want!

Think about 'what makes you sad' and reflect on your coping strategies.

List the things you do to lift your mood.

At the end of the book are written down a few thoughts – you might find some items coincide with your list; you might even come across a novel idea to try out next time you feel 'down in the dumps'.

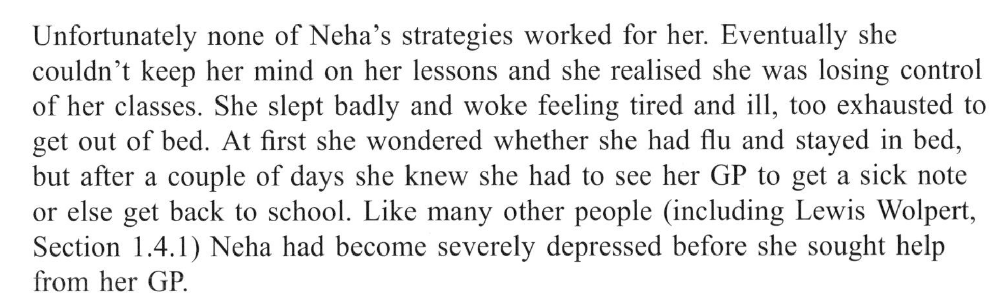

Unfortunately none of Neha's strategies worked for her. Eventually she couldn't keep her mind on her lessons and she realised she was losing control of her classes. She slept badly and woke feeling tired and ill, too exhausted to get out of bed. At first she wondered whether she had flu and stayed in bed, but after a couple of days she knew she had to see her GP to get a sick note or else get back to school. Like many other people (including Lewis Wolpert, Section 1.4.1) Neha had become severely depressed before she sought help from her GP.

Like Neha, most people will experience at least one potentially traumatic event, such as death of a loved one, in the course of their life. After a period of grief and sadness the majority will adapt to the new situation and return to living life much as before. They are said to exhibit **resilience**. In the next section we turn to a consideration of what it is that predisposes some people to exhibit resilience.

3.2.1 Resilience

Resilience is defined as the ability to recover quickly from adverse events or stressful changes. In the 1970s academic interest in this concept sprung from studies of children who thrived and developed life competencies, becoming physically and psychologically well-adjusted adults, despite living in appalling environments, both physical and emotional (e.g. extreme poverty, chronic maltreatment). The children who thrived despite chronic adverse circumstances were characterised as being active and alert with attractive personalities; that is, they were affectionate and good-natured. This enabled them to elicit help and support from suitable adults such as caregivers from the extended family as well as teachers and youth workers. As they grew older they developed good communication and problem-solving skills. They were outgoing but emotionally sensitive with a positive self-image. They had a coping strategy of self-help combined with the ability to seek help from appropriate sources when necessary. In later life they were often attached to effective support systems; belonging to religious groups, the armed services or taking opportunities for adult education. They usually had a supportive friend or partner.

More recently the concept of psychological resilience has been investigated with respect to adults who experience potentially traumatic events. Bonanno (2004, pp. 20–21) defines resilience to potential trauma as 'the ability of adults in otherwise normal circumstances who are exposed to an isolated and potentially highly disruptive event such as death of a close relation or a violent or life-threatening situation to maintain relatively stable, healthy levels of psychological and physical functioning, as well as the capacity for generative experiences and positive emotions'. Resilience is contrasted with **recovery**, where individuals do not remain in good psychological health following the trauma but are subsequently able to return to baseline levels of functioning (see Figure 3.2).

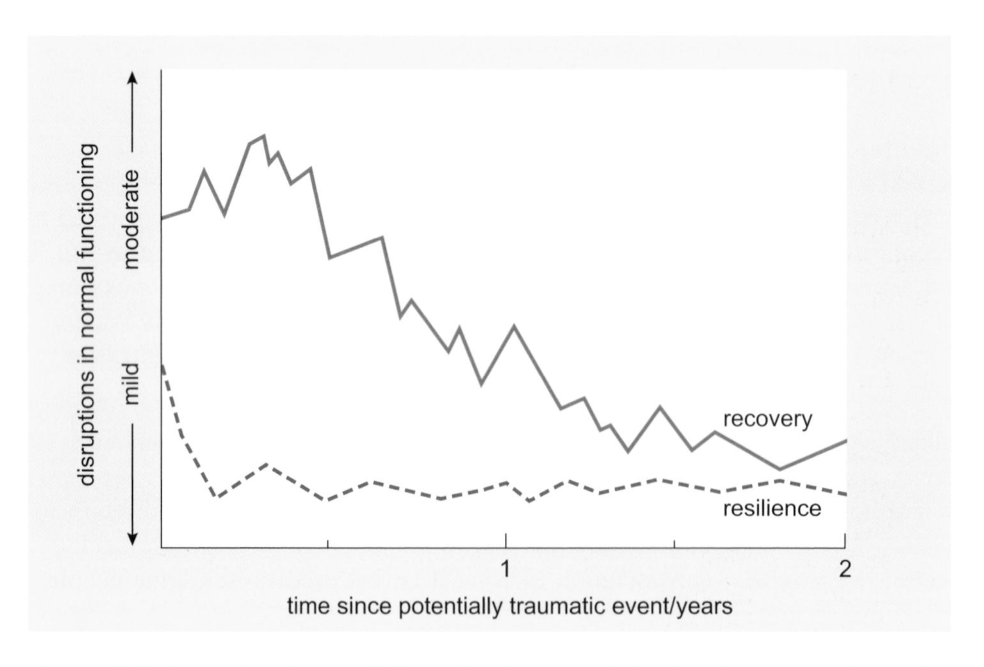

Figure 3.2 Typical patterns of disruption in normal functioning across time after potentially traumatic events.

Researchers have found, that as with resilience in children, resilience in adults can be acquired by numerous and different routes. For example, some people will take a pragmatic approach to the potentially traumatic event. They will be self-centred and goal-directed, adopting the attitude that they will cope 'whatever it takes'. By contrast, an approach that is successful for others is termed 'repressive coping' where the individual avoids unpleasant emotional experiences. For yet other people a flexible adaptation to the new situation works. In addition to this is the likelihood that some people will have a genetic predisposition to exhibit resilience. The key finding is that resilience is far more common than was previously supposed, suggesting that interventions are not necessary and may interfere with the natural process of dealing with traumatic events (Bonanno and Mancini, 2008). Partly as a consequence of this, the immediate treatment of victims caught up in violent and potentially traumatic events – known as *critical incident stress debriefing* – has now fallen out of favour because there is little evidence that debriefing decreases the incidence of post-traumatic stress disorder (PTSD) and because there are concerns that being counselled by strangers in the aftermath of a tragedy may be emotionally painful and unhelpful to those who are not at risk of PTSD.

However, although there are a number of effective coping strategies, such as taking exercise, that people use to improve their emotional state, and despite the fact that the majority of people exhibit resilience and are able to continue to function well despite facing potentially traumatic events such as the death of a loved one, there are times when events overwhelm and treatment is sought.

3.3 Treatment for depression

In Section 1.4.1 you read Professor Lewis Wolpert's account of his experience of entering into a state of severe depression. Now read Vignette 3.1 to find out what he has to say about his treatment.

Vignette 3.1 Lewis Wolpert's treatment

He wrote this account after he had woken up with a compulsion to kill himself – his family got him straight into a psychogeriatric ward – where it was peaceful and he felt looked after.

> My psychiatrist put me on Seroxat and assured me I would recover – I did not believe her.
>
> I spent most of the time in bed for the first few days doing relaxation exercises, and then they let me go for little walks with a companion. They tried to give me cognitive therapy but it made no sense at that stage. I accepted that all my views were negative but this seemed perfectly natural considering the condition I was in. I thought of suicide all the time [...] I kept asking for ECT [...] as I thought the drug would not work.
>
> Over a period of three weeks I improved a bit and cognitive therapy began in the last week to make some sense. I returned home but remained indoors most of the time.
>
> [...]
>
> I had cognitive therapy once a week and began to consider going back to work but was frightened I would not be able to cope. There was a meeting that I considered attending but was frightened I would panic and walk out. My therapist did a scenario with me about the meeting in which I walked out but the others did not mind. This enabled me to go and I survived and this was an important step in my recovery

Seroxat® is an SSRI.

ECT is described in Section 3.3.3.

St Johns Wort is a plant. Herbalists use it as an antidepressant and it can be bought 'over the counter' in the UK. Side effects include headaches, nausea and raised blood pressure.

> [...]
>
> But my recovery from my severe depression was not the end [...] Four years later [...] some of the symptoms of depression came back for no obvious reason. I tried St Johns Wort but that did not help.
>
> I returned to my cognitive therapist who thought I was anxious about my impending retirement [...] Things got worse and my psychiatrist put me back on Seroxat and my decline continued. There were panic attacks and a cold tingling feeling would spread over my skin. I tried exercise which usually made me feel better but this made me feel exhausted and I entered a half-sleep state when I no longer had control of my thoughts. I felt I was going insane.
>
> [...]
>
> My new partner [...] found my condition very hard to deal with and she persuaded me against my will to consult a psychoanalyst. She had to drive me there and pick me up as I could not travel on my own. I refused to lie on the couch and found the interaction unfriendly, quite unlike my relationship with my cognitive therapist. Also I think psychoanalysis is without any scientific foundation. Fortunately after several weeks he took a long winter break and I got much better and did not go back. Since then there have been further episodes but none really severe and I was prescribed Effexor (venlafaxine) which I am still on. Exercise also works well for me.
>
> *(Wolpert, 2009, pp.1–2)*

Venlafaxine (marketed as Effexor®) is a serotonin-noradrenalin reuptake inhibitor (SNRI).

In the account given by Lewis Wolpert a point to notice is that he was not offered one single treatment for his depression. He was offered, sought out and used a variety of treatments. Some treatments worked for him at specific stages in his illness but not at other stages. Some treatments never worked for him but have helped other people with depression.

The National Institute for Health and Clinical Excellence (NICE) is an independent body that provides evidence-based guidance on promotion of health and treatment of ill-health.

Within the UK NHS system, 2004 NICE guidelines propose a **stepped-care model** for depression (see Figure 3.3). If the least intrusive treatments bring no relief, then treatment is 'stepped up' to a more intensive treatment.

The first step is for the GP to recognise and make an accurate assessment of the presence of, and severity of depression. This model is therefore based on an assumption that the GP will be instantly aware that the patient is depressed. As you have already read in this book (Section 1.5.1), many people will focus on their physical (somatic) symptoms and within an appointment of 5 or maybe 10 minutes even a good GP, who will carry out appropriate physical and physiological tests, may miss the fact that the root of the problem is depression. On the other hand, there are the people who 'self-diagnose', read about their supposed problem on the internet, and turn up at the surgery demanding antidepressant medication (ADM). In the face of such certainty the time-pressured GP is likely to prescribe pills for them rather than carry out a full assessment. The estimates are that around 19% of those who

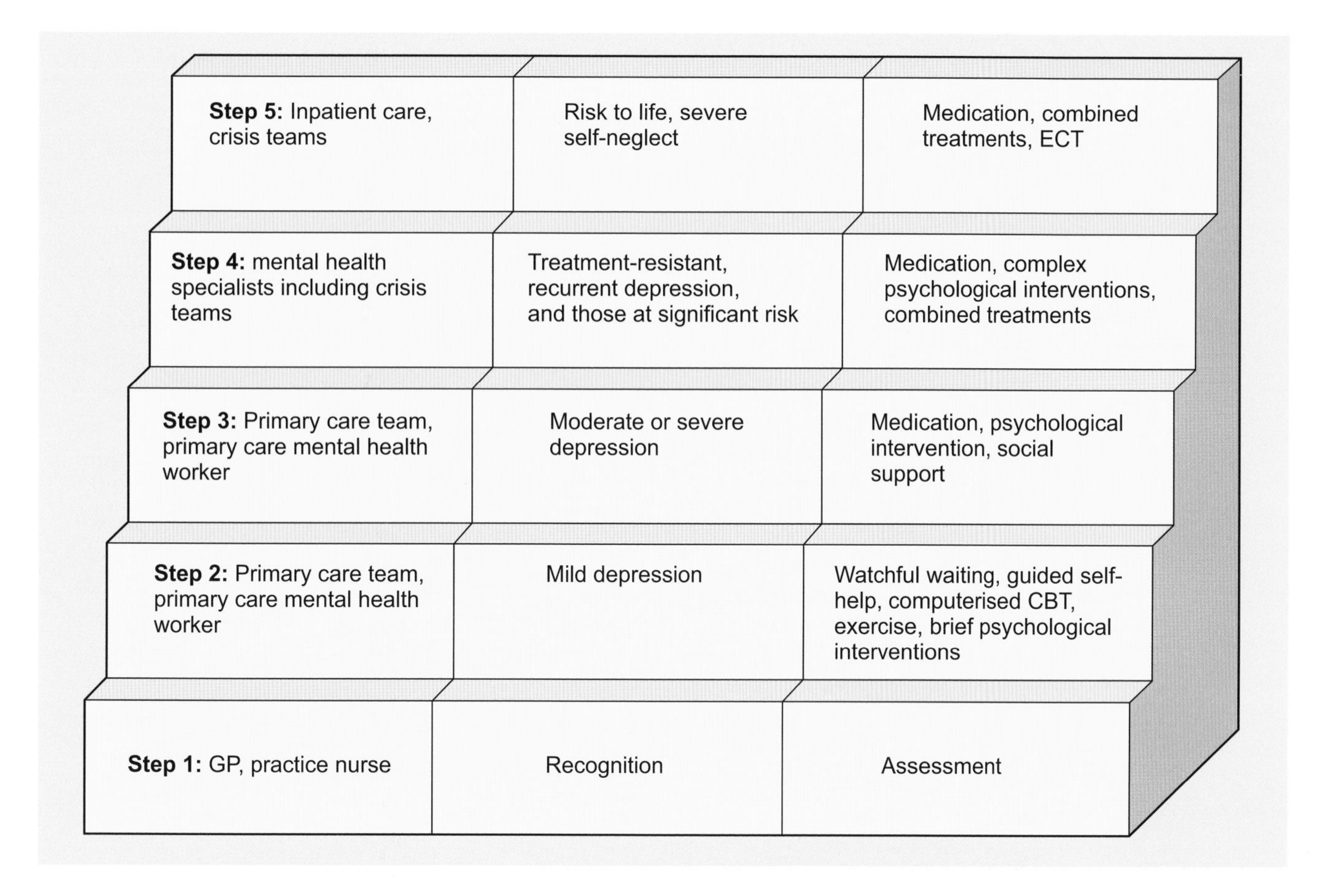

Figure 3.3 This model, adapted from the NICE stepped-care model for depression (published in 2004 and subsequently updated in 2009), provides a framework by which practitioners can identify the most effective interventions for different severities of depression and for those for whom treatment has yet to deliver benefits.

are receiving treatment for depression are not depressed and 50% of those who need treatment are missed at the first appointment (Section 1.5.1).

- ■ Looking at Figure 3.3, do you think it is ever appropriate for a GP to prescribe ADM for a patient who walks into the surgery requesting it?
- □ Yes, it may be appropriate because NICE guidelines recommend ADM for moderate or severe depression. However NICE does not recommend medication for mild depression, so undoubtedly there will be some people who request and receive ADM inappropriately.

3.3.1 Treating mild depression

Figure 3.3 suggests ‘exercise’, ‘watchful waiting’ and ‘guided self-help’ as the GP’s first approach for treating mild depression. If Neha had been only mildly depressed when she first went to the GP she might have come away with some general advice (increasing the amount of exercise she took perhaps) and/or leaflets giving advice and names of self-help organisations – including those that have activities on websites – both nationally and locally. Her experience would depend very much on the GP’s interest and experience of

A PCT operates within the NHS to provide health care for a particular community.

this area of medicine as well as what was available within her Primary Care Trust (PCT).

It would perhaps also depend on how well the GP knew her or was able to assess accurately her interests and volition.

Figure 3.3 also shows that 'brief psychological interventions' and/or 'computerised cognitive behaviour therapy' (CCBT) are options recommended for mild depression. It is known that patients prefer psychological interventions to medication and that psychological interventions are effective (Department of Health, 2001). A problem is the shortage of suitably trained individuals to deliver these therapies. As a response the NICE guidelines (2004) suggest interventions that use health technologies such as guided self-help and CCBT requiring minimal or no therapist input. If these interventions are not successful, then treatment can be 'stepped up' to more intensive therapies. With guided self-help the patient does most of the work using a guided manual (or workbook). A therapist or trainee therapist will make infrequent and brief (around 15 minutes) contact to check on progress. For these interventions to succeed, it is important that the therapist or GP has clearly explained their purpose and dealt with unrealistic expectations before the therapy starts. In particular the depressed person is often looking for answers to the question: 'Why has this happened to *me*?' This is not a question that will be addressed by these minimal interventions which, by contrast, are aimed at symptom control (Macdonald et al., 2007). In Activity 3.3 you will explore and experience a computer-based therapy.

Activity 3.3 'Living Life to the Full'

(LO 3.1) Allow 1 hour

Now would be an ideal time to experience the computer-based therapy in the multimedia map. This is a link to a course that is free to use and is endorsed by the NHS.

'Living Life to the Full' (experienced in Activity 3.3) was devised by Dr Chris Williams, a psychiatrist based in Glasgow, and is one of the minimal psychological interventions advised in Step 2 in the NICE guidelines (2004). Such interventions are based on therapies that use the cognitive model. This model, first espoused by Albert Ellis (1913–2007) and Aaron Beck (1921–) is based on the supposition that psychopathology is a function of dysfunctional beliefs and ideas about oneself. For example, believing oneself to be worthless and incapable of carrying out any activity effectively leads to feelings of depression. Any type of **cognitive therapy (CT)** will aim to address these negative thoughts, to challenge them and to replace them with more positive thoughts and ideas about oneself. The way you think about an event or situation will influence how you behave. So the therapy of choice is currently **cognitive behaviour therapy (CBT)** because it does not just address flawed thinking but will seek to alter dysfunctional behaviour (i.e. what you do).

What you do will in turn affect how you think and how you feel physically and emotionally. Note how this relates to the 'five areas' assessment (shown in Figure 3.4) discussed in the 'Starting out' module of 'Living Life to the Full'.

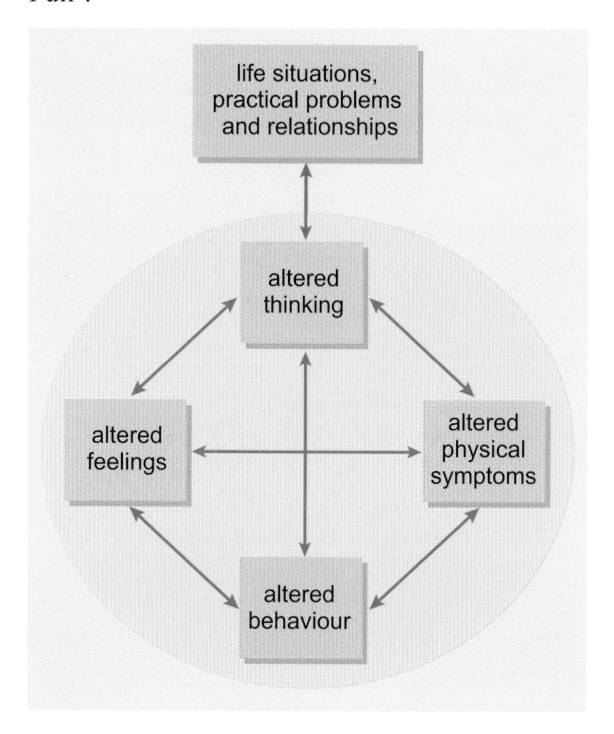

Figure 3.4 The 'five areas' assessment. The circle represents the individual.

CBT deals with the present, the 'here and now'. It doesn't try to use past events or experiences from childhood to explain the way you feel or act now. It works by breaking down an unpleasant experience into small pieces, seeing how the pieces interconnect, and how at every stage there are alternatives (thoughts and actions) available. The therapist will then suggest behaviours that can be tried out to test the beliefs. For example, Joan, in the 'Living Life to the Full' 'Starting out' module, had stopped opening the door to her family because she thought they would be thinking that her husband had left her because she was a terrible wife. The therapist might point out that doing this cuts her off from potential sources of support and suggest that her 'homework' should be to open the door next time a family member calls round and invite them in for coffee and a chat. She might also be asked to write down what they talked about and how her mood and feelings were (a) when she opened the door, and (b) whilst talking.

Although in this section, a clear distinction has been made between CT and CBT, in practice a cognitive therapist may provide some practical behaviour 'tips' whilst a therapist using CBT might not always send their client away with behaviour homework. The relationship between any therapist and their client is confidential and unique. This can make it difficult for researchers to assess the usefulness of a particular therapy in an objective way, a point you should bear in mind when reading such accounts.

In Activity 3.3 you saw how the CBT approach could be applied. Now read Box 3.2 which is an example from the Royal College of Psychiatrists website.

Box 3.2 Applying CBT techniques to an everyday situation

The following example is used to explain CBT and is taken from the Royal College of Psychiatrists website (2010), where more information can be found.

Situation:	You've had a bad day, feel fed up, so go out shopping. As you walk down the road, someone you know walks by and, apparently, ignores you.	
	Unhelpful	**Helpful**
Thoughts:	He/she ignored me – they don't like me	He/she looks a bit wrapped up in themselves – I wonder if there's something wrong?
Emotional: Feelings	Low, sad and rejected	Concerned for the other person
Physical:	Stomach cramps, low energy, feel sick	None – feel comfortable
Action:	Go home and avoid them	Get in touch to make sure they're OK

The same situation has led to two very different results, depending on how you thought about the situation. How you *think* has affected how you *felt* and what you did. In the example in the left hand column, you've jumped to a conclusion without very much evidence for it – and this matters, because it's led to:

- a number of uncomfortable feelings
- an unhelpful behaviour.

If you go home feeling depressed, you'll probably brood on what has happened and feel worse. If you get in touch with the other person, there's a good chance you'll feel better about yourself. If you don't, you won't have the chance to correct any misunderstandings about what they think of you – and you will probably feel worse. This is a simplified way of looking at what happens. The whole sequence, and parts of it, can also feedback like this [Figure 3.5]:

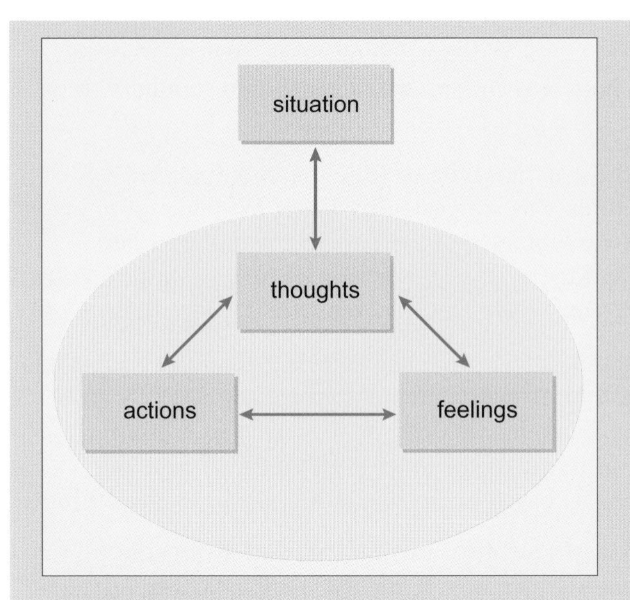

[Figure 3.5] A vicious circle.

This 'vicious circle' can make you feel worse. It can even create new situations that make you feel worse. You can start to believe quite unrealistic (and unpleasant) things about yourself. This happens because, when we are distressed, we are more likely to jump to conclusions and to interpret things in extreme and unhelpful ways.

CBT can help you to break this vicious circle of altered thinking, feelings and behaviour. When you see the parts of the sequence clearly, you can change them – and so change the way you feel. CBT aims to get you to a point where you can 'do it yourself', and work out your own ways of tackling these problems.

(Royal College of Psychiatrists, 2010)

- ■ Having read Box 3.2 and carried out Activity 3.3, say how the 'vicious circle' differs from the 'five areas' assessment?

- □ In the vicious circle, emotional and physical feelings have been placed in a single category although they are separate in the scenario reported.

It is useful to keep the two areas of emotional and physical feelings separate because although we know that physical symptoms (such as those associated with flu or an adrenalin rush) can alter emotional feelings, they do not do so in the consistent way that is implied by having only one category.

- ■ The scenario of meeting someone who ignores you, used by the Royal College of Psychiatrists, is virtually the same as that used in the 'Living Life to the Full' module. What is the crucial difference?

- □ 'Living Life to the Full' suggests that if you knew the person was facing personal difficulties you would react differently.

Often the depressed person does not have the necessary information to know why someone else behaves in a particular way. It is therefore really important for them to understand, as Dr Chris Williams emphasises, that it is not the event that causes upset but how it is interpreted. This should remind you of Selye's notion of stress and 'how you take it' in Section 2.2.3.

As you saw from Activity 3.3 it is possible to follow a computerised CBT programme on your own but, as was suggested by Chris Williams, it is better if you can have the support of another person. This can sometimes be arranged through the NHS and there is evidence that with the help of a trained therapist, computerised CBT can lift depression (see Box 3.3 and Figure 3.6).

Working alone with a workbook or on a computer does not suit everyone and there are other 'brief psychological interventions' that can be used for mild depression. These tend to be therapies that can be delivered to a group, making them cost-effective in terms of the amount of therapist time per person. One such intervention is based on a technique known as **mindfulness**.

Mindfulness can be defined as a receptive attention to, and awareness of, present events and experience (Brown and Ryan, 2003). It is a form of self-awareness training that has been adapted from Buddhist meditation. Mindfulness involves effortless concentration and full attentiveness to what is being experienced at a particular moment. The idea is simply to allow oneself to be absorbed in the here and now, rather than being mentally transported elsewhere. There is more on mindfulness in the next chapter.

Mindfulness-based cognitive therapy (MBCT) is a group intervention where, in addition to learning mindfulness meditation techniques, participants are also introduced to simple cognitive behaviour therapy principles underlying constructive thinking. Supported by several randomised controlled trials (RCT; Box 3.3), MBCT emerges as a powerful approach to mood regulation (Teasdale et al., 2000) and a relapse prevention therapy for those recovering from depression (Shapiro, 2009). A multi-centre RCT was used to allocate 145 recovered participants to either treatment as usual or the same treatment supplemented by MBCT.

In this context, recovery is usually defined as 6 months symptom-free.

After receiving 8 weeks of classes, participants were followed up for 12 months. The results showed that MBCT did help those who had suffered depression episodes on a number of occasions, reducing the risk of relapse in those who had had three or more previous episodes from 66% to 37% (Teasdale et al., 2000).

Box 3.3 Research Methods: Randomised controlled trials

When seeking to evaluate a therapy or a drug, the 'gold standard' approach is to conduct a **randomised controlled trial (RCT)**. In an RCT; *randomised* means patients are randomly allocated to treatment groups and *controlled* means that one group (the experimental group) receives the treatment of interest and their outcomes are compared with those of the other group (the control group) who have some kind of matched experience but do not receive the treatment of interest. As an example, consider the RCT that investigated the effectiveness of a computerised CBT treatment called 'Beating the Blues' (Proudfoot et al., 2004).

Potential participants were screened whilst sitting in GPs' waiting rooms. On the basis of their responses to health questionnaires they were invited to take part in the study if they were assessed as being mildly depressed. They were enrolled to the study provided they were willing to attend eight 1-hour sessions at their local surgery to work on the computer, were not receiving any other psychotherapy or counselling and had not taken antidepressant medication for a period of 6 months or more. Random allocation to treatment or control group was carried out in the following way:

At each surgery the practice nurse sorted participants into groups based on whether or not they were taking antidepressant medication, and whether their current emotional disorder had lasted up to 6 months or more than 6 months.

Within each of these groups, whether or not the individual would receive the computerised CBT treatment was based on the information on a card inside a sealed envelope.

The cards (computer therapy or treatment as usual) were randomly sorted by the researchers, then each card was placed in a sealed envelope and numbered.

The practice nurses were given sufficient envelopes for the number of participants recruited from their surgery and instructed to open the envelopes in strict numerical order.

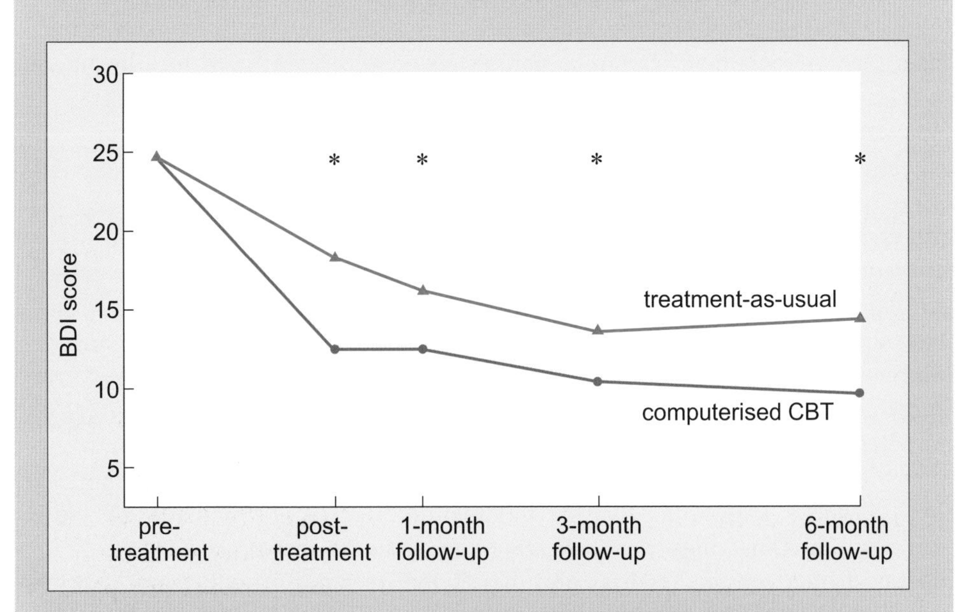

Figure 3.6 The improvement of mood (as ascertained using the Beck Depression Inventory (BDI)) over time for two treatment groups: a treatment-as-usual group and a computerised CBT group. * denotes a statistically significant difference between the BDI scores of those in the two groups.

This RCT involved 274 patients (Proudfoot et al., 2004) Those who were chosen to receive the computerised CBT took part in an 8-week programme of weekly 50-minute interactive computer sessions. The practice nurse spent about 5 minutes with the participants at the start and conclusion of each session to check they had everything they needed (including their 'homework'!) and to answer any queries. Both groups continued to see their GPs and were treated by the GPs in whatever way seemed appropriate (e.g. further physical investigations, medication and/or general advice and practical and social help), but the computerised CBT group were not offered any other form of counselling or psychotherapy.

This study showed that this particular computerised CBT works better than placebo (i.e. the treatment-as-usual/control condition) for depression (see Figure 3.6).

3.3.2 Treating moderate to severe depression

Antidepressant medication (ADM) is recommended for moderate and severe depression. In Section 2.3, the idea that depression might be linked to reduced levels of the monoamines serotonin and noradrenalin within the brain was considered.

■ What role do these substances have within the brain?

□ Serotonin and noradrenalin are neurotransmitters found in the brain. They operate at synapses, enabling communication between neurons.

Therefore, one method of counteracting depression might be to increase levels of these neurotransmitters. Two types of ADM do just that. Both MAOIs (monoamine oxidase inhibitors such as isoniazid, see Section 2.3.1) and tricyclics (so called because their chemical structure has three rings) have their effect on the brain by increasing levels of serotonin and noradrenalin, although they achieve this by differing mechanisms, as is shown in the animations associated with Activity 3.4. More recent ADMs are the selective serotonin reuptake inhibitors (SSRIs) such as fluoxetine (marketed as Prozac®) that only affect levels of serotonin, and the serotonin-noradrenalin reuptake inhibitors (SNRIs) such as imipramine (Section 2.3.1) and venlafaxine (marketed as Effexor®) that affect the levels of both serotonin and noradrenalin. Although the levels of neurotransmitters increase very shortly after the patient has taken the tablets, the therapeutic effect (if any) is not seen for 3–5 weeks, suggesting that the therapeutic effect is not mediated by the immediate pharmacological effect. One suggestion is that neurogenesis is increased by these medications and that BDNF (a brain growth factor) may be involved (Section 2.3.1).

■ How are levels of BDNF affected by depression?

□ Levels of BDNF appear to be abnormally low in patients with major depression.

Activity 3.4 ADM effects at synapses

(LO 3.2) Allow 20–30 minutes

Now is an ideal time to listen to the audio clip and study the animations associated with this activity in the multimedia map. Follow the instructions given in the activity.

As you have just heard SSRIs and SNRIs are the drugs most likely to be initially prescribed. These ADMs do not work for everyone and subsequently tricyclics and even the more general MAOIs will be tried. Fewer than 50% of patients will achieve full recovery (defined as 6 months symptom-free), after using one ADM. However, by trying different formulations and mixes of drugs a medication that reduces symptoms can be found for almost everyone (DeRubeis et al., 2008). There is evidence that these ADMs are effective when compared to placebos such as a sugar-coated pill but not that they are more effective than cognitive therapies (see Figure 3.7).

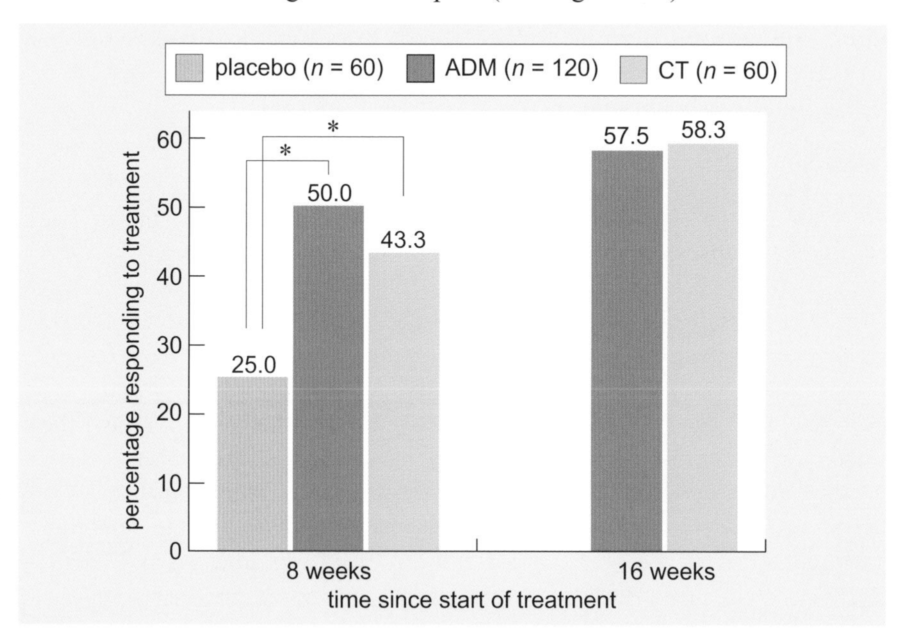

Figure 3.7 Comparison of treatment with cognitive therapy (CT) and antidepressant medication (ADM) to placebo. (Note that placebo was discontinued after 8 weeks.) The number of participants in each group, *n*, is also given. * denotes a statistically significant difference (at 8 weeks) between the percentage of those responding to treatment in the ADM and in the CT groups compared to those in the placebo group.

Figure 3.7 shows the response of outpatients who had moderate to severe depression to cognitive therapy (CT), ADM or placebo. Patients who were assigned to ADM or CT showed a significantly higher response rate after 8 weeks of treatment than those who were assigned placebo. After 16 weeks the response rate of ADM and CT were almost identical. Figure 3.8 shows what happened to these patients in the longer term.

In the longer term, only the patients who had responded to treatment were kept in the study. Those who had responded to cognitive therapy were allowed a maximum of a further three sessions of CT over the continuation period and were given no treatment in the subsequent 12 months. Those who had responded to ADM were randomly allocated to one of two groups. One group was taken off ADM but given the sugar-coated pill (placebo) whilst the other group continued with the ADM for the continuation period, after which, if they were still well, ADM was withdrawn.

Figure 3.8 shows that the group given ADM subsequently divided into two groups: those who carried on taking the medication (the compliant group) and those who stopped taking the medicine. It is a feature that bedevils much treatment and research in medicine that patients do not always follow the advice given. They do not necessarily admit to this! If treatment involves taking medication, then sometimes a blood test can reveal whether instructions are being followed. In this experimental study there was no significant difference between those who continued to the end with ADM versus those who stopped taking it at some point. Both groups fared better than the group on placebo. The group that gained most benefit from treatment was the group that had had cognitive therapy (CT). Recall that this CT treatment was for 16 weeks only at the beginning of the 2-year study period.

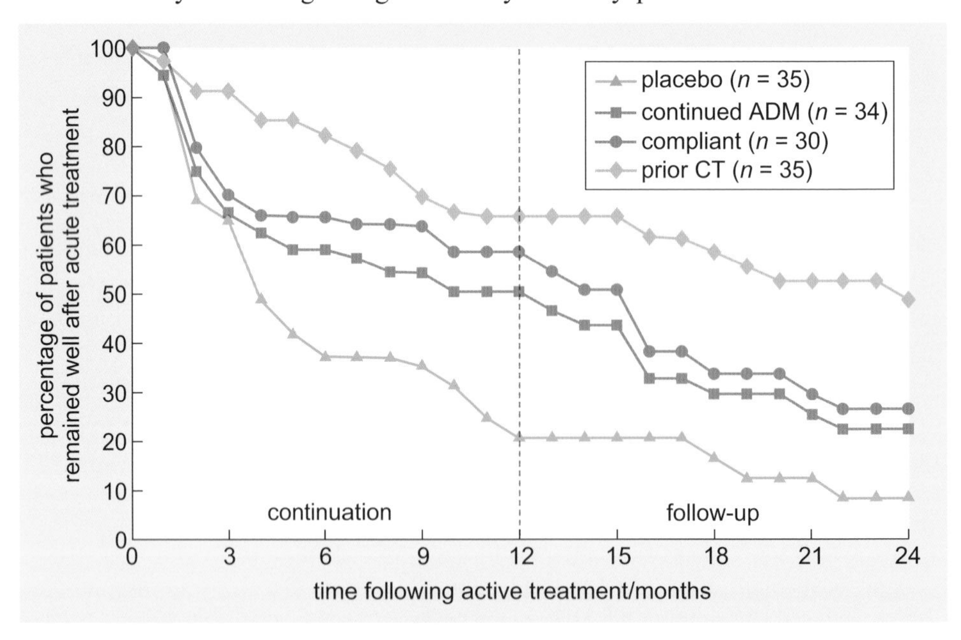

Figure 3.8 The health of participants in the 2 years following the treatment with cognitive therapy (CT), antidepressant medication (ADM) or placebo. These are the same groups whose results are shown in Figure 3.7. The number of participants in each group, n, is also given.

- ■ Look at Figure 3.8 and say what percentage of the CT group were still well after 2 years.
- □ Around 50% were still well.

- ■ Use the information in Figures 3.7 and 3.8 to say how many of the 60 people who received CT were still well after 2 years.
- □ About 18 were still well. (25 individuals showed no improvement with CT. Only the 35 individuals who responded to the CT treatment were followed over the 2 years.)

It can be rather easy when looking at a graph such as Figure 3.8 to feel optimistic about recovery from depression but the truth is that, at the moment, neither ADM nor CT is delivering great gains and the likelihood of suffering from a further bout of depression is about five times greater than for the general population. In the UK only about 1 in 4 people with depression are receiving any kind of treatment and it is claimed that most episodes resolve without treatment (DeRubeis et al., 2008). Indeed, some investigations into the effects of CT do not show consistently good results and this is often attributed to the variability in the skill of the therapist. Yet, there is one undisputed advantage of CT versus ADM: CT has no known adverse side effects (see Table 3.1).

Table 3.1 Common side effects of ADM.

Type of medication	Examples*	Some side effects
Tricyclics	imipramine (Tofranil®)	Anxiety, dry mouth, gastric disorders, constipation, fatigue, sexual dysfunction, weight gain, blurred vision, lowered blood pressure (hypotension), increased risk of heart attack and stroke
Monoamine oxidase inhibitors (MAOIs)	iproniazid (Iporzid®) phenelzine (Nardil®)	Dry mouth, dizziness, raised blood pressure (hypertension) headaches and nausea
Selective serotonin reuptake inhibitors (SSRIs)	fluoxetine (Prozac®) paraxetine (Seroxat®)	Anxiety, fatigue, headaches, gastric disorders, dizziness, sleeping difficulties, sexual dysfunction
Serotonin-noradrenalin reuptake inhibitors (SNRIs)	venlafaxine (Effexor®)	Anxiety, fatigue, headaches, gastric disorders, dizziness, sleeping difficulties, sexual dysfunction
Lithium†		Fatigue, blurred vision, tremors, irregular heart beat (cardiac arrhythmias)

* Names in brackets are the trade names of drugs.
† Lithium is used for bipolar disorder. It stabilises mood, preventing both depressive and manic phases. It is very effective, usually benefiting around 80% of those with a diagnosis of bipolar disorder. It is taken continuously but has to be carefully monitored because it is toxic.

The fact that ADMs have side effects should not be too surprising after reading, in the previous chapter (Section 2.3), that many of them have been discovered when a drug being investigated or used for quite other reasons is found to either cause or alleviate depression. Taking a tablet orally (by mouth) into the body allows the drug access to all of the body systems. From inside the gut the drug crosses the wall of the gut and enters the bloodstream and is distributed around all of the body via the circulatory system. In mental health conditions, the desired physiological region of action is obviously the brain. There is a particular difficulty associated with targeting the brain specifically as this organ is surrounded by a protective layer called the **blood–brain barrier** which acts to prevent substances in the circulatory system from entering the brain itself (see Box 3.4).

Box 3.4 The blood–brain barrier

Although he did not pose the existence of the blood–brain barrier himself, Paul Ehrlich was the first to show that it existed when he injected blue dye into the circulatory system of rats. His experiment showed that, although most of the tissue in other organs throughout the body stained blue, the tissue of the brain and spinal cord did not. The term 'blood–brain barrier' actually refers to the lining of the small blood vessels that supply blood to the central nervous system. This lining is made by cells that fit very tightly together, preventing large molecules from passing in between them and into the brain tissue itself. The organisation of these cells can be seen in Figure 3.9. In this way, the blood–brain barrier is not a total barrier but is very selective in that only some molecules may cross. The blood–brain barrier protects the brain.

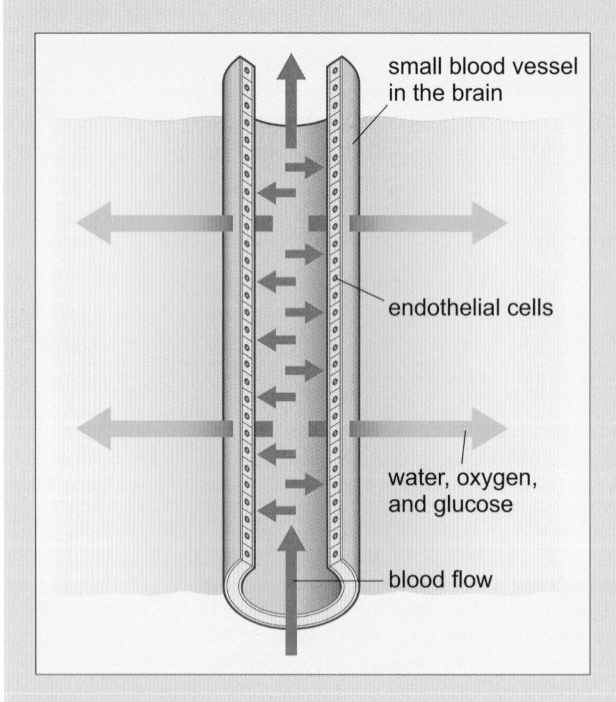

Figure 3.9 The blood–brain barrier.

The blood–brain barrier therefore presents a problem to those who are developing drugs for the treatment of mental health conditions because in order to get enough of the drug into the brain there will be far greater amounts circulating around the body where it may interact with other physiological systems generating effects that are known as side effects because they are not the desired effects (Book 1, Section 2.4.1). Thus when reserpine was used to control high blood pressure, small amounts entered the brain and depression was the undesired side effect. Conversely, the drug isoniazid used to treat tuberculosis had the beneficial side effect of being a monoamine oxidase inhibitor.

3.3.3 Treating intractable depression

There are a few people who do not respond to any kind of ADM or cognitive therapy. When these people have severe depression, particularly if they are suicidal, then electroconvulsive therapy (ECT) may be considered. ECT is administered briefly (for less than a second) by passing an electric current through the head of the anaesthetised patient, thereby bringing about a brain seizure – uncontrolled electrical activity. The rationale for trying this treatment in the first place was the observation that depressed patients who were also prone to epileptic fits showed an improvement in mood after a fit – which is essentially a brain seizure. Treatment is usually given two or three times a week for several weeks. The majority of reports suggest that the treatment brings immediate relief to around half of those treated. A review of randomised control trials (Pagnin et al., 2004) suggested that ECT was superior to ADM. However, in the longer term the benefit is often not maintained, leading to claims that ECT is no better than placebo (a sham ECT) (Ross, 2006).

A sham ECT is where the patient has electrodes applied to the head and is put under a light anaesthetic, just as they would be if ECT were to be administered, but no current is turned on.

Whilst ECT is a controversial treatment – side effects can include confusion and a substantial loss of memory – some depressed people gain enormous relief with the immediate lifting of depression and removal of suicidal thoughts.

A more recent therapy for intractable depression is **deep brain stimulation (DBS)**. DBS has been likened to a brain pacemaker. A small device, implanted in the upper chest, contains a battery-powered generator that can be connected to brain structures by thin wires passed just beneath the surface of the skin, up the neck and then into the brain (Figure 3.10).

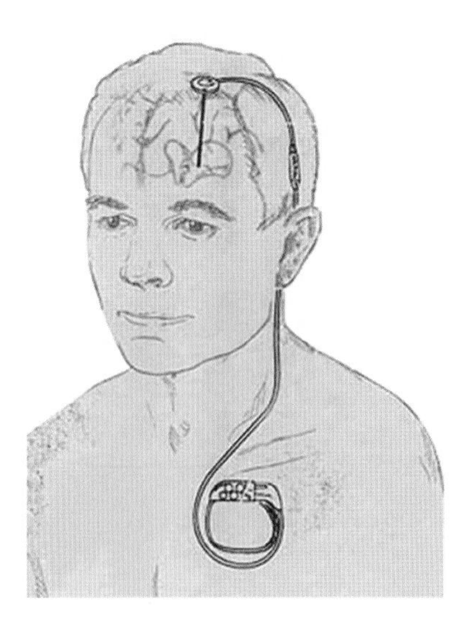

Figure 3.10 Diagram showing where deep brain stimulation equipment is inserted into the body.

After surgery, the patient remains in hospital whilst the dose is monitored and adjusted as needed. Only a handful of people have received the treatment so far, so long-term effects and safety cannot be properly judged; however, the signs are very encouraging. Patients talk of experiencing 'intense calm and relief', of the 'heavy dread in the pit of the stomach' disappearing and of 'black clouds lifting'. Treatment is continuous and the benefits seem to remain. In the next section you will learn how the brain area for DBS was chosen.

3.4 How do treatments work?

The short answer (given in Book 1, Section 2.4.1 in relation to Prozac®) is that we don't know. Nevertheless, the previous chapter indicated some possible pathways by which treatments, both drug and psychotherapy, might

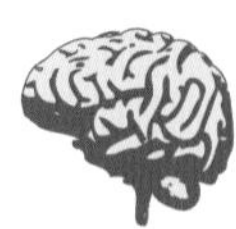

be able to alter brain structure and function to elevate mood. We assume that if either a biological treatment (e.g. ADM) or a psychological treatment (e.g. CT) has consequences for mental events (e.g. improves mood), then there will also have been changes in brain events (e.g. increased level of activity in the prefrontal cortex).

There have been a number of imaging studies that investigate brain activity pre- and post-treatment and are suggestive of the possibility that ADM and psychological treatments achieve their effects by different routes. In other words, different mechanisms are involved in eliminating symptoms. Goldapple et al. (2004) found that, in general, frontal cortex activity (including the prefrontal cortex) decreased while hippocampal activity increased with CBT and the reverse was found with ADM (Figure 3.11).

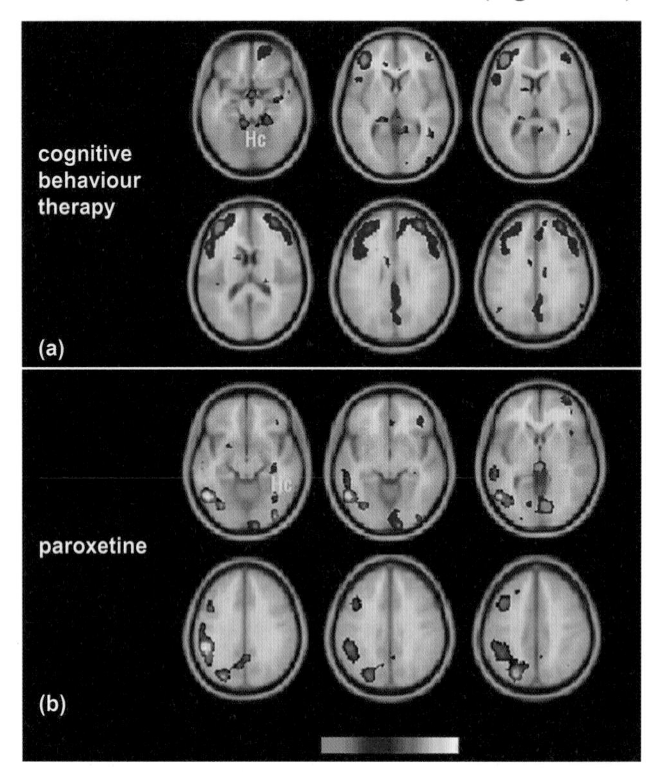

Figure 3.11 Scans showing activity in brain regions after (a) CBT and (b) SSRI treatment. Increased activity is shown as orange, decreased activity as blue. After CBT the hippocampus (Hc) shows increased activity (orange) whilst the areas showing decreased activity (blue) are mainly in the frontal cortex. By contrast areas of the cortex show increased activity after successful treatment with the SSRI paroxetine and there is reduced activity in the hippocampus, although you might notice that this effect is not an exact reversal because the precise regions of the Hc and PFC do not correspond. These images are horizontal sections which means that they can be thought of as looking down into the brain from the top of the head.

The fact that relapse is less likely after CT is discontinued than after ADM is discontinued (see, for example, Figure 3.8) further supports the idea that the treatments affect the brain in different ways. Goldapple suggests that CBT has targeted and modified the destructive negative thoughts under the conscious control of activity in the prefrontal cortex whilst ADMs alter activity in the emotional brain areas such as the hippocampus.

A consistent finding relates to the role of an area of the cortex called the subgenual cingulate cortex which is found to be overactive in the brains of depressed individuals. Mayberg and colleagues (2005) targeted this area based on imaging studies for their successful DBS treatment.

Several studies have shown that mood improvement is associated with neurogenesis and that ECT too may stimulate such growth (Mann, 2005; Section 2.3.3), but another possibility for the beneficial effect of ECT is that it causes an increase in the release of GABA, an inhibitory neurotransmitter (Section 2.2.6) which might influence the activity of the amygdala (see Section 3.5).

A factor not yet considered is that ill-health is seldom 'neat'. Reading and listening to personal accounts you will have been struck by the range of symptoms experienced by any one person. Depression is often experienced with (i.e. is comorbid with) anxiety. It is to the treatment of anxiety that we now turn.

3.5 Treating anxiety disorders

Anxiety disorders encompass many problem areas for individuals and there is a very high occurrence of comorbidity both within this group of disorders and between depression and anxiety (Figure 1.12). Additionally, from your reading of Chapter 1 you should be aware that symptoms are rarely straightforward and thus diagnosis is seldom immediately unequivocal.

Chapman (1997) suggests that specific phobias or 'unreasonable fears' affect over half of the population. If you reflect for a moment you may be able to identify an 'unreasonable fear' to which you are prone. However, for most people this fear is contained and does not prevent them from living a normal life. Just as unreasonable fears of specific objects or events can assail most people from time to time, so too can non-specific bouts of worrying. It is difficult to explain why, for some people, this can develop into the chronic and pathological condition known as generalised anxiety disorder (GAD). In Vignette 1.2 of this book you met Suzanna who was making no progress in controlling her GAD and was unable to work.

In the next two sections you will look in more detail at treatments offered for GAD and some specific phobias.

3.5.1 Treatments for general anxiety disorders (GAD)

Like many people with a diagnosis of GAD, Suzanna experiences numerous physical symptoms (Vignette 1.2). She has also had bad experiences when trying to elicit help. You can read about these in Vignette 3.2.

Vignette 3.2 Suzanna's treatments

> My own personal experience within the NHS dealing with this condition is traumatic to say the least. I have only just managed to beg a locum at my GP's office to refer me to a behavioural therapist. None of the other doctors had heard of behavioural therapy and one of my GP's actually said that he did not believe in 'alternative therapies'
>
> [...]
>
> I have been given tablet after tablet over the course of the past 2 years. Beta Blockers for tachychardia, diazepam (an anxiolytic drug), seroxat (a SSRI) and more.
>
> None have worked. I am no better and now feel no longer able to go to the GP ... I have had over 20 ECGs and a 24 hour monitor [both procedures monitor heart activity]. I only received the ECG's because I ended up going to casualty thinking I was having a heart attack, so many times. I am now told by my GP nurse (who was the only one who took me seriously and arranged to refer me), that I have been referred to a behavioural therapist.
>
> *(Anxiety UK, 2007)*

Tachycardia is a rapid heart rate – usually above 100 beats per minute.

Anxiolytic drugs are prescribed to reduce anxiety.

■ Now that Suzanna has a referral what might be the next stage in the treatment process? (Book 1, Section 4.1.2).

□ Ideally, a case formulation will be prepared.

Suzanna claims to have been given 'tablet after tablet' and NICE guidelines for GAD (NICE, 2007) suggest that anxiolytic drugs such as diazepam should only be prescribed for short periods (2–4 weeks at most) and they ought to bring immediate relief. These drugs enhance the inhibitory effect of GABA on the amygdala, which is rich in GABA receptors, and overactivity in which is closely linked with depression and anxiety (Section 2.2.6); they act as a sedative and muscle relaxant, so the individual should become relaxed and their anxiety should be reduced. This does not seem to have worked for Suzanna. The second line of medication suggested by NICE is SSRIs, such as Seroxat®. If this does not improve the condition it should be discontinued after 12 weeks. This didn't work for Suzanna either. As with depression, CBT is the psychological therapy of choice. The individual should be offered 16–20 hours, in weekly sessions of 1–2 hours and all within a 4-month period. Although medications did not work for Suzanna, it is to be hoped that the behaviour therapy will help her.

Activity 3.5 Treating depression and anxiety disorders holistically

(LOs 3.1, 3.2, 3.3 and 3.4) Allow 45 minutes

Now would be an ideal time to watch the video clips associated with this activity in the multimedia map.

3.5.2 Treating specific phobias

Treatments often relate to favoured explanations for the aetiology of a condition. Phobias have been recognised for a long time as being disturbed ways of thinking, and the most straightforward, common-sense suggestion for their acquisition is that they are learned. My friend has a dog phobia – he tells people that this is because a dog bit him when he was a child. That sounds perfectly reasonable, and may well be true, but I also was bitten by a dog when I was a child. I remember the horror of the teeth stuck in my thigh and the hot blood running down my leg, but I am not now afraid of dogs. I tell people that this is because I now know the worst that can happen – and that too may be the correct reason for *my* lack of dog phobia. It does, however, illustrate the point that it is important to remember that we are all different – different genes, different upbringing – and so it is unsurprising if we achieve good or poor mental health through different routes. This is one reason why it is important for anyone offering a therapeutic solution to a mental health problem to keep an open mind and to explore with each individual possible reasons for their poor health, rather than assume that all cases can be explained by a single process and therefore cured by one specific type of treatment.

Nevertheless, it appears true that some phobias are acquired as a consequence of a learning process and probably the first recorded example (1920) is the story of 'Little Albert' (Figure 3.12). The way that 'Little Albert' was treated would be deemed unethical today but his story is one of the classic tales in the psychology literature. Albert was a stolid, usually unemotional, 11-month-old infant who, having been seated on a mattress between two experimenters, was offered a tame white rat. He had been shown the rat 2 months previously and had not reacted unfavourably towards it. This time he reached out and just as he touched the rat the experimenters hit a steel bar behind Albert's head, with a hammer. The dreadful noise caused the child to recoil from the rat and he fell forward and buried his face in the mattress. The experimenters repeated the procedure and this time Albert whimpered as well as turning away from the rat. A week later Albert was offered the rat and he reacted somewhat ambivalently towards it. So the experimenters went on to offer the rat three more times, each time also clanging the bar with the hammer. After this, the fifth presentation of the rat caused young Albert to whimper even though this time the experimenters did not clang the bar.

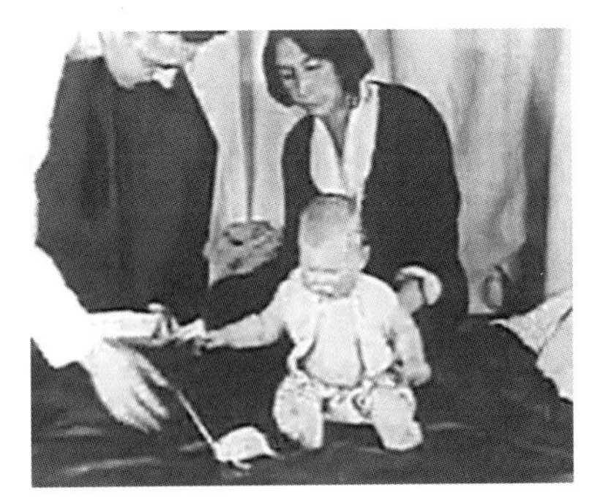

Figure 3.12 Little Albert with Watson (standing) and Rayner (seated).

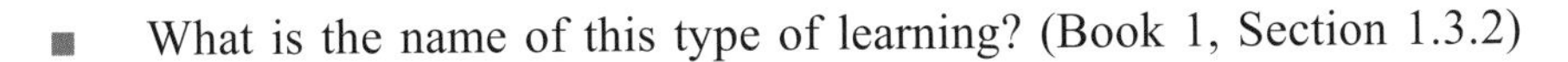

- What is the name of this type of learning? (Book 1, Section 1.3.2)

□ This is an example of classical conditioning.

■ How would you describe an experiment that has only one participant? (Book 1, Section 4.3)

□ This is a case report.

Whilst giving some useful insights, case reports are rather weak as scientific evidence because they are based on only one individual. In this particular case, early efforts to replicate the findings were unsuccessful and subsequently the protocol was considered unethical, so no further attempts were made to repeat the experiment.

It is not universally accepted that Watson and Rayner did induce a phobia in Albert, but for now we will continue with him as our example.

Any therapist who knew that Albert's phobia had been brought about by classical conditioning would have a sound theoretical basis for treatment.

■ What procedure would the therapist apply to treat Albert's phobia? (Book 1, Section 1.3.2)

□ The therapist would try to extinguish the conditioned response to the white rat.

Extinguishing a conditioned response involves presenting the conditional stimulus (the rat) without the unconditional stimulus (loud noise) many times until finally the rat produces no fearful response. There has already been mention of the way that this is tackled in a clinical situation for people with a spider phobia. The procedure is known as graded exposure (or exposure therapy) (Book 1, Section 2.2.2).

■ How does graded exposure differ from extinction?

□ In graded exposure Albert would not be immediately presented with a rat; he would initially be shown pictures of a rat, held some distance away from him, but then gradually moved closer. Then he might be shown a model rat, again initially held far away from him. Finally, he would be able to touch a live rat.

Graded exposure is a therapy that is frequently used, particularly for the treatment of specific phobias. Graded exposure does not work for everybody. Some people find that their fear increases the more they experience the stimulus of which they are afraid. This clinical phenomenon is known as *incubation*.

Although dog phobias are often reported to be a consequence of an unpleasant early experience, a number of other phobias, such as snake phobia, are rarely a consequence of a frightening experience. It has been suggested that snake phobia and a number of other specific phobias might have an evolutionary origin rather than being a learned response to an unpleasant early experience. The idea is this: in past times snakes would have represented a threat to humans, so anyone who reacted rapidly and in a way that minimised the chance that the snake inflicted any damage would be likely to survive. Having survived, they would in time have children who might inherit this useful characteristic.

There is some evidence from twin studies, for a genetic predisposition for specific animal phobias (Kendler et al., 1992) – which is, of course, a necessary prerequisite for any evolutionary theory (Section 1.3). The effect is not very strong and its relative importance decreases with age (Kendler et al., 2008).

A suggestion that refines the evolutionary explanation is that we are biologically prepared to respond differently to different stimuli. So stimuli such as fast flowing rivers and cliff edges, spiders and snakes might represent real dangers and children would naturally avoid them. As time passes and they experience no harm, they learn how to exist safely alongside these stimuli. Thus their early fear is overcome and it is only people with dysfunctional habituation responses (they do not become used to these stimuli) who become phobic for these situations and objects. Some evidence for this comes from the Dunedin Study, a prospective, longitudinal study (Book 1, Box 4.5) of 1037 children in the town of Dunedin in New Zealand who were born between 1 April 1972 and 31 March 1973. It was found that young adults with phobias of water or of height were not those who as children had had traumatic experiences with these elements. Quite the reverse; those who had had unpleasant experiences such as falling from heights and sustaining damage seemed to have less fear of heights than most. On the other hand, young people who were scared of heights had apparently experienced fewer accidents such as falling off things or falling down stairs (Poulton and Menzies, 2002). The authors noted that retrospective studies bore this out; they could find little evidence of height or water phobias being explained as a consequence of a traumatic earlier experience with these elements. Thus they proposed a **non-associative fear acquisition model** whereby certain biologically relevant stimuli readily evoked fear and could subsequently become the focus of a phobia if normal developmental maturation did not take place.

Another theory with a biological basis is the **disease avoidance model** of animal phobias (Matchett and Davey, 1991). The authors of this theory noticed that those people who had animal phobias often were also very inclined to show strong 'disgust' responses. Disgust is a food-rejection emotion that predisposes to reject (or spit out) items that might be contaminated and thereby decreases the chance of succumbing to poisoning. So a range of animals might be avoided because contact with them would increase the chance of acquiring a disease. Reasons for showing disgust and avoiding an animal might relate to their appearance, (e.g. slugs because they are slimy) or to the stories told about them (e.g. rats and maggots because they carry disease) and others might be avoided by association (e.g. mice, larvae) (see Figure 3.13).

Despite this range of ideas about how someone comes to acquire a phobia, most therapists use some version of graded exposure as a treatment. The theory behind this is straightforward. The phobic object or situation is usually acknowledged to be irrationally feared (one of the DSM-IV-TR criteria for specific phobias), so it is necessary to change cognition from irrational fear to

Figure 3.13 A range of common phobic objects and situations.

a belief that it is truly innocuous. This could be achieved by learning – repeated pairing of the feared object (or situation) with no unpleasant effect. At the same time, the therapist could expose and challenge the fears, getting the patient to think carefully about their reasons for being afraid and to assess what the true danger level is. For example: 'what is the worst damage that this spider could inflict on me?' Answer: 'it might run over my skin and tickle me'; 'what is the worst thing that could happen to me if I go into this small space?' Answer: 'I might not be able to get out immediately if the door stuck'. Changing one's thinking by means of challenging dysfunctional thoughts and beliefs is known as **cognitive restructuring**.

Activity 3.6 Treating phobias

(LOs 3.1 and 3.3) Allow 20 minutes

Now would be an ideal time to watch the video clips associated with this activity in the multimedia map. Follow the instructions in the activity.

3.5.3 Assessing the efficacy of treatment for anxiety disorders

If a treatment is to be used, the patient wants to know whether there is a reasonable expectation of an improvement in their condition. Ost and colleagues (2001) were interested in the answer to this question in relation to the type of therapy used and also in the mode of delivery. They wanted to know whether cognitive behaviour therapy could deliver benefits for people with claustrophobia. They also wanted to know whether exposure therapy was best delivered in one intensive session or in shorter sessions over a longer time period. For this study they recruited 46 individuals whose fear of enclosed spaces was affecting daily living. Individuals were randomly assigned to one of four groups:

E1 – these individuals had one 3-hour session of exposure therapy.

E5 – these individuals had five sessions of exposure therapy a week apart; each session lasted an hour and there was homework.

C5 – these individuals had five sessions of cognitive behaviour therapy a week apart; each session lasted an hour and there was homework.

WL – these individuals were on a waiting list for 5 weeks before they were offered therapy.

Before treatment started, all individuals were given a battery of tests; these included:

- self-assessment questionnaires
- physiological tests
- behavioural tests.

These tests were then carried out again after 5 weeks when all treatments had finished and were repeated a year later. As an example, individuals were tested in three situations:

1 Taking a lift to the top of a nine-storey building and then back down again.

2 Entering a small windowless room (a WC) and remaining locked in for 5 minutes.

3 Wearing and breathing through a gas mask for 5 minutes.

Participants could end the test whenever they felt necessary.

■ The results of one of these tests is given in Figure 3.14. What type of test is this (see above for the types of test used), and what sort of measure has been obtained?

□ This is a behavioural test (as are tests 1 and 3 above). The researchers have obtained a quantitative measure of the participants' behaviour in a standardised situation.

■ Physiological tests included measuring heart rate and blood pressure. Why are these relevant measures?

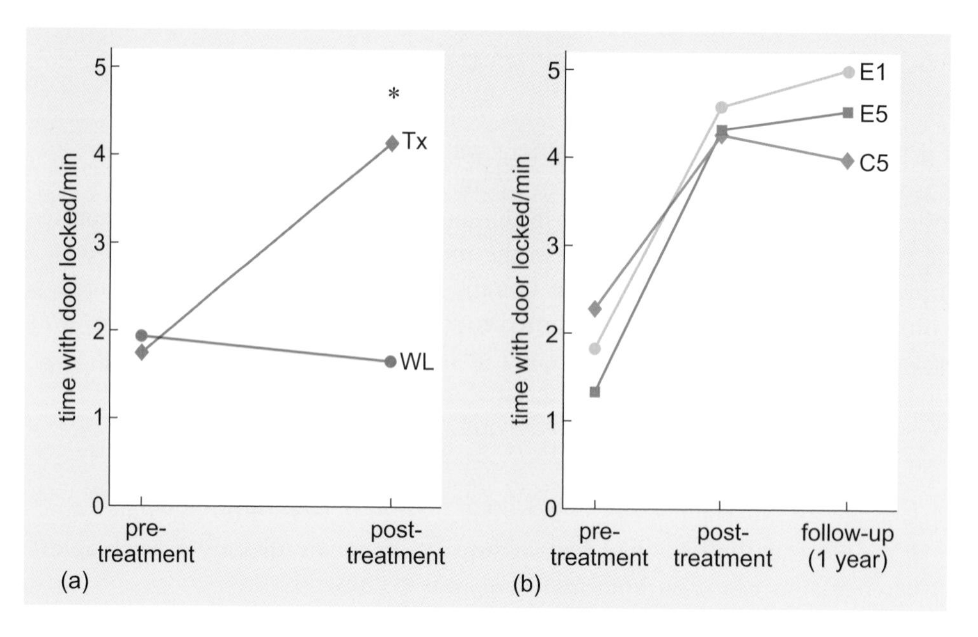

Figure 3.14 (a) The amount of time that the two groups were able to spend in the small windowless room before treatment (pre-treatment) and after a 5-week period (post-treatment). Tx is the treatment groups (i.e. groups E1, E5, C5) and WL is the group that received no treatment. * denotes a statistically significant difference in the time spent indoors by those in the Tx and WL groups. (b) The results for the three different treatment groups separately and at 1 year after the original treatment. (See the text for explanations of the three types of treatment, E1, E5 and C5.)

□ These are measures of the functioning of the autonomic nervous system (ANS) and could give an indication of the extent of stress that was being experienced (Book 1, Section 2.5.3, and Section 2.2.6 in this book).

■ Now look more closely at Figure 3.14a. All those who received treatment have been combined into a single group called Tx and their behaviour has been compared to those who were receiving no treatment. Describe the outcome of this treatment.

□ After 5 weeks in therapy the treatment group participants were able to spend, on average, 4 minutes locked into the WC whereas before treatment participants averaged only 2 minutes before letting themselves out of the small room. Participants who received no treatment showed no improvement in their ability to remain in the small room.

There was a small difference between the three treatment groups as can be seen in Figure 3.14b. The difference between the performances of these three groups is not statistically significant.

As mentioned, the test described was just one of many tests and questionnaires used to assess each individual's state pre- and post-treatment. It was also used as an exposure exercise. In exposure a number of fearful situations are directly experienced with the help of the therapist, whereas in cognitive therapy the fearful situations are discussed with the therapist who then suggests alternative ways of thinking about the situation. After treatment, all the tests and questionnaires were used again and a composite rating was given. This indicated that post-treatment 79% of those in the treatment groups had improved to a **clinically significant** extent. A clinically significant improvement is seen when a treatment results in the participant responding in a way that falls within the range of responses given by those who do not need treatment. However, for some mental health conditions this range of responses is just not currently possible so the definition of a clinically significant outcome has to be altered (e.g. for neurodegenerative disorders such as dementia, discussed in Book 4).

Interestingly 18% in the non-treatment group (WL) also showed clinically significant improvement. Nevertheless, overall the treatment groups showed a statistically significant difference from the non-treatment group. Improvements were shown by 80% of those in the E1 group, 81% in E5, 79% in C5 and 18% in WL. When tested 1 year later, these measures were 100%, 81% and 93%, respectively, for the treatment groups.

As there were no statistically significant differences between treatment groups, Ost and colleagues concluded that CBT was a useful therapy for specific phobias but suggested that a single-session exposure therapy would be the most cost-effective treatment for phobia. Subsequently other studies have agreed with this. Before moving on, reflect on what you would consider to be a successful outcome for someone suffering from claustrophobia and look at Figure 3.15.

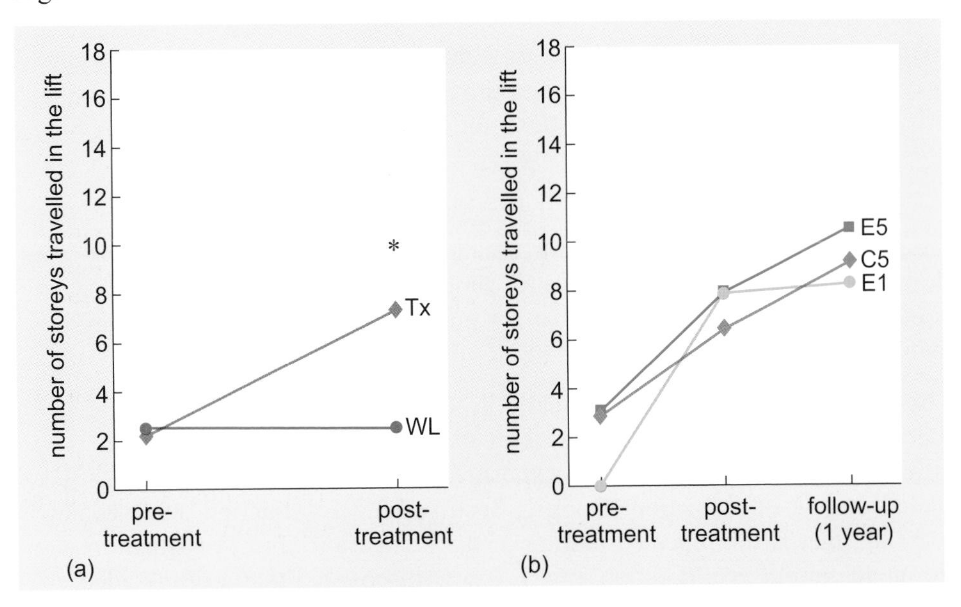

Figure 3.15 Results from the elevator test. (a) The amount of time spent in the elevator (measured as the number of storeys travelled) before treatment (pre-treatment) and after a 5-week period (post-treatment). * denotes a statistically significant difference in the number of storeys travelled in the lift by those in the Tx and WL groups. (b) The results for the three different treatment groups separately and at 1 year after the original treatment. (See the text for explanations of the three types of treatment, E1, E5 and C5.)

Figure 3.15 shows that, on average, following CBT these participants were still not able to remain in a lift long enough for it to carry them 18 storeys. So despite this being a statistically significant improvement you may wonder whether this represents an effective treatment outcome from the participants' point of view. Probably the most important outcome is their subjective assessment of the treatment – are they now able to do all the things they couldn't do before and need to do to enjoy life. It isn't possible to discover that from perusing the data given in this figure, but composite ratings did take this kind of information derived from the self-assessment questionnaires into account.

Choy et al. (2007) reviewed treatments of specific phobias in adults and one point they make is worth reflecting upon when reading accounts of successful treatment. Sadly, many people who are offered exposure therapies do not participate. Either they withdraw before treatment begins or they cease to cooperate before the treatment is complete. If you read personal narratives on the internet you will notice that many people report being unable to make even the first step towards recovery; they are afraid to seek help from their GP or to confide in friends. Thus what is being reported is the success of a treatment for those who fully participate. It often ignores those who dropped out and/or the even larger group of people who never participated. Once again this emphasises the importance of volition; recovery does not begin until the individual applies volition – you can't have good done unto you!

Using psychological theories to identify some of the possible causes of specific phobias has led to the implementation of various reasonably successful behaviour and psychological therapies, as you have seen. So you may be wondering whether what is known about the underlying brain processes can lead to any suggestions for drug treatments.

3.5.4 Drugs and the brain: insights into specific phobias

Drugs are not widely used in the treatment of specific phobias. In a few cases drugs to reduce anxiety can be useful short-term emergency measures (e.g. if someone with a fear of flying must get on a plane), but they merely mask symptoms and do not provide a long-term solution.

There is one drug that is occasionally used in conjunction with exposure therapy and it was recruited because of its role in learning (Richardson et al., 2004). As you now know, exposure therapies are based on an understanding of extinction (Book 1, Section 1.3.2). Extinction involves new learning, that is the repeated pairing of the unpleasant object or situation with no unpleasant effects (Section 3.5.2). It was discovered that a drug called D-cycloserine (DCS) improved the extinction of learned fear in rats. This drug works particularly well when the dose is given just after an extinction training session. In other words, the drug is facilitating the consolidation of the new learning. Although not widely used at the time of writing (2010), there are reports of success and further trials being carried out to evaluate its utility and mode of action.

The brain area where DCS is active – at least in rats – is the basolateral amygdala (Lee et al., 2006). This relates well to the finding that some individuals with specific phobias have abnormalities in serotonin and dopamine pathways, especially involving the amygdala (Stein, 1998).

So if DCS is to be used, one question is whether other studies of brain activity in those being treated by therapies based on extinction techniques also found changes occurring in the amygdala. In Book 1, Chapter 2 you read of a study that investigated where brain changes were observed after successful CBT for spider phobia (Paquette et al., 2003). Reread Section 2.2.2 in Book 1 to remind yourself how this study was conducted and also note whether a change in activity in the basolateral amygdala was observed.

The account in Book 1 only mentions changes in the prefrontal cortex (PFC) in the right hemisphere of the brain (refer to Figure 2.12 in Book 1). Paquette and colleagues had formulated a hypothesis concerning this brain area, based on previous studies including one that had showed that people with spider phobia behaved in one of two ways when watching a video of live spiders. They either showed severe panic (and activity *decreased* in the right dorsolateral prefrontal cortex) or they were frightened but not panic-stricken (and activity *increased* in the right dorsolateral prefrontal cortex). It was hypothesised that this increased activity represented efforts being made by these individuals to control their behaviour; that is, they were using 'cognitive strategies for coping with the phobic situation' (Paquette et al., 2003). So, because of what was previously known, Paquette and colleagues looked to see whether successful CBT would result in changing activation in the PFC, hippocampus and visual association cortex but not in the amygdala. They found that after CBT neither the PFC nor the hippocampal areas were significantly activated. They interpret this to mean that CBT has changed the way the individual views the spider. It no longer evokes fearful memories and so there is no need for the activation of the cognitive strategy for coping with a fearful situation. (Incidentally, there were two suggestions for the decreased activity seen in the right PFC of the panic-stricken individuals: either that cognitive processes related to escape were active, or that the cognitive processes were trying to 'blank out' the situation.)

Although Paquette and colleagues did not report any effect on the amygdala, other studies of spider phobia have shown such effects. Schienle and colleagues (2009) were investigating changes not just immediately after successful CBT but also longer term, 6 months later. They found that the behavioural gains from the treatment were maintained, but were surprised that activation of the amygdala remained the same after CBT as before CBT treatment. (This might be because activation is very brief and they don't 'catch it' with their experimental techniques.) However, they found increased activity in the medial orbitofrontal cortex, an area that is associated with learning positive associations, and they link this finding to the pleasure and pride that the participants expressed at being able to hold spiders in the hand without experiencing fear after the CBT. So perhaps it is this sense of satisfaction that keeps alive the learning brought about by CBT, and it may be that DCS can assist in consolidating learning in this brain area too.

In conclusion, there may be a small role for drugs such as DCS in treatment of specific phobia, but they have no therapeutic value on their own and are only helpful as an adjunct whilst CBT is being given.

3.6 Final word

At the beginning of this chapter it was observed that some people possess resilience in the face of potential trauma. To an extent, vulnerability is genetically determined (Chapter 2) but there is also the possibility of 'training' for resilience. There are certain activities that can help protect against emotional disorders. If you spent some time exploring the 'Living Life to the Full' modules you will have gained a good understanding of the kinds of 'life skills' that can help to protect you from emotional disorders.

There is also the role you can play in other people's lives. Friends and relatives can provide positive, ongoing support for people recovering from depression and anxiety and can help them to maintain good mental health. However, it is not always easy to give appropriate support. Remember that Neha was a member of a supportive and caring extended family, yet she felt that their phone calls were unhelpful and that they simply told her to 'pull herself together'. In part this may have been her negative interpretation of what they were saying. However, despite best intentions it is easy to become frustrated with a loved one who is constantly belittling themselves whilst you are trying to bolster their self-confidence.

Sometimes support from people you know less well can be effective; for example, a religious or social organisation or a club. Many people find online group forums to be helpful or that joining a self-help group can be a positive step, and the Samaritans is a well-known organisation that caters for those who are feeling low as well as those who are suicidal. Already you have read how meditation, exercise, social and interpersonal attachments can help people maintain good psychological health. There is more about this in the next chapter of this book.

3.7 Summary of Chapter 3

- There are a number of effective coping strategies, such as taking exercise, that people use to improve their emotional state.
- The majority of people exhibit resilience and are able to continue to function well despite facing potentially traumatic events such as the death of a loved one.
- NICE suggests a stepped-care model for the treatment of depression.
- There is evidence that various types of cognitive therapy, including computerised CBT, can be as effective as medication in the treatment of depression, and better than placebo.
- Different types of treatments suit different people. None of the treatments for depression is effective for more than around 50% of the people who are offered them and there is evidence that different treatments affect the brain in different ways.
- For some of those with severe, intractable depression electroconvulsive therapy provides immediate relief. There are early signs that deep brain stimulation is equally successful and has fewer side effects.

- GAD is difficult to treat; NICE suggests anxiolytic drugs for acute treatment followed by short-term use of SSRIs and CBT.
- Classical conditioning, biological preparedness, non-association fear acquisition and disease avoidance models have all been proposed to explain specific phobias.
- The therapist's approach to treating specific phobias is informed by their preferred aetiological explanation, but some kind of graded exposure to the phobic object or situation is usually incorporated into the treatment.
- Specific phobias can often be treated equally successfully with one session of graded exposure therapy as with a course of CBT.

3.8 Learning outcomes

LO 3.1 Describe the different types of psychological treatments available for emotional disorders and when they might be used. (KS3, KS4)

LO 3.2 Describe the different pharmacological treatments that may be used in treating emotional disorders and when they could be employed. (KS3, KS4)

LO 3.3 Describe how you might evaluate the effectiveness of a treatment for an emotional disorder. (KS4)

LO 3.4 Recognise the importance of the individual and society in treating emotional disorders. (KS3, KS4)

3.9 Self-assessment questions

SAQ 3.1 (LOs 3.1 and 3.2)

John (Book 1, Section 1.1.1) has had obsessive–compulsive disorder (OCD) for 5 years. Although this is putting a strain on family relations John is in work and manages to control his compulsion during work hours. He also manages to get to work on time. (This is something that can be a problem for many people with the type of OCD that pushes them to constantly check that they have done things properly – such as locking the house or turning off the gas/electricity.)

(a) What kind of emotional disorder is OCD?

(b) What kind of medication and what kind of therapy would be suitable to treat John's OCD?

SAQ 3.2 (LO 3.2)

Can you think of any justification for prescribing ADM on demand to people with mild depression?

SAQ 3.3 (LO 3.3)

There were three behavioural tests used by Ost and colleagues (2001) (Section 3.5.3) as part of their evaluation of the effectiveness of CBT as a treatment for claustrophobia. Explain which test appears to have the least good external validity.

SAQ 3.4 (LO 3.4)

Post-traumatic stress disorder (PTSD) was accepted as an emotional disorder in 1980 with DSM-III although in past times the description of 'shell shock' was used to describe PTSD symptoms. The lifetime prevalence rate is relatively low (around 1%–3%), given that it is estimated that half the population will experience an event that could precipitate PTSD during their life. What is the characteristic that protects against psychopathology precipitated by potentially traumatic events?

Chapter 4 Positive psychology: the science of well-being

Ilona Boniwell and Claire Rostron

4.1 Introduction

So far in Chapters 1, 2 and 3 we have considered emotional disorders, highlighting the benefits of a biopsychosocial approach. This chapter, rather than focusing on *disorder*, will cover the principles of *positive* psychology (Book 1, Section 1.1.2), a branch of psychology that concerns itself with the application of scientific principles to the study of human happiness. Research in this area therefore has relevance to the study of mental health in terms of understanding how the development of mental health problems might be prevented. Positive psychology, however, also places emphasis on personal growth and the potential of individuals, and on researching the things that 'make life worth living'. It is often summarised in the words of its founders, Martin Seligman and Mihaly Csikszentmihalyi, as

> [the] scientific study of optimal human functioning [that] aims to discover and promote the factors that allow individuals and communities to thrive.
>
> *(Seligman, and Csikszentmihalyi, 2000, p. 5)*

4.1.1 The rationale behind positive psychology

According to positive psychologists, for most of its life mainstream psychology (sometimes also referred to as 'psychology as usual') has been concerned with the negative aspects of human life without any serious consideration of the positive aspects. This state of affairs came about through a historical accident. Prior to World War II, psychology had three tasks. These were to cure mental illness, to improve normal lives, and to identify and nurture high talent. However, with the horrors of World War II resulting in thousands of veterans returning home from combat and suffering from flashbacks and dissociation (see Figure 4.1), the last two tasks of psychology became de-emphasised. (The term 'dissociation' refers to a detachment of the mind from reality.)

Figure 4.1 The experience of many soldiers involved in combat in World War II was so severe that thousands returned home with mental health problems, shifting the focus in psychology very much towards the treatment of mental ill-health.

This left the field to concentrate predominantly on the first one: the treatment of mental health problems (Seligman and Csikszentmihalyi, 2000). This is how psychology as a field came to operate within a disease (or biomedical) model.

Seligman, one of the founders of positive psychology, highlights the victories of this particular model, including that many aspects of human suffering (diagnosed as 'mental illness', such as depression, personality disorder or anxiety attacks) are now better understood, with a range of pharmacological treatments available. You may have your own views on whether these can indeed be seen as 'victories'! Alternatively, the costs of adopting this disease model resulted in the negative view of psychologists as 'victimologists' and 'pathologisers', and the failure to address the improvement of normal lives and the identification and nurturance of high talent. Far from negating the importance of 'psychology as usual', however, positive psychology proposes to concentrate on those two areas that have not yet received adequate scientific attention.

The term 'nurturance' refers to the provision of physical and emotional care.

Importantly, therefore, positive psychology is still nothing else but psychology and it adopts and utilises some of the same methods. It simply studies different topics and poses slightly different questions, such as 'what works?' rather than 'what doesn't?', 'what is right with this person?' rather than 'what is wrong?', 'why do some individuals succeed when faced with unfavourable circumstances?' instead of 'why do some fail?'

4.1.2 The historical roots of positive psychology

Positive psychology places a lot of emphasis on being a new and forward-thinking discipline. Whilst the second claim might be true, the idea of focusing on the positive aspects of life is not new.

The roots of positive psychology can be traced as far back as the thoughts of the Ancient Greek philosophers. Aristotle, for example, believed that there was a unique *daimon*, or spirit, within each individual which guides us to pursue things that are right for us. Acting in accordance with this *daimon* is what leads one to happiness. The question of happiness has since been picked up by hundreds, if not thousands, of prominent thinkers, and has given rise to many theories including **hedonism**, with its emphasis on maximising pleasure, and **utilitarianism**, which seeks the greatest happiness for the greatest number.

Figure 4.2 Marie Jahoda (1907–2001) was an extremely influential thinker in the field of social psychology. She was concerned with understanding the psychological effects of life experiences such as employment and unemployment and the meaning of work, as well as race relations and prejudice.

Another influence on positive psychology that is rarely acknowledged comes from the Eastern traditions of Hinduism and Buddhism. Loving kindness, compassion and joy, which are the emotions explicitly promoted by these traditions as the paths to happiness, are in themselves major areas of research in modern positive psychology. Various Buddhist approaches offer many different methods for cultivating positive emotions. Nowadays, many of these practices and techniques, such as yoga, mindfulness (Section 3.3.1) and meditation, claim a prominent place in the field of positive psychology having been the subject of randomised controlled trials (Levine, 2000).

■ What is a randomised controlled trial?

□ RCTs involve the random allocation of participants to two or more groups and comparing the proposed intervention with another condition intended as a placebo (Box 3.3).

In the 20th century, many prominent psychologists also focused on what later became the subject matter of positive psychology. Amongst them was Marie Jahoda (Figure 4.2), who was concerned with identifying the characteristics of individuals that experience 'ideal mental health' (Jahoda, 1958).

Another prominent exception to the historically negative emphasis within psychology was the famous American behavioural psychologist Burrhus F. Skinner. His emphasis was on the process of reinforcement of behaviour (see Book 1, Section 1.3.2) and on opposition to aversive methods of control, as in punishing wrong-doing. Skinner believed that a Utopian society could be designed based upon the avoidance of aversive controls. Such a society would achieve the maximum degree of happiness for all its citizens (Toates, 2009).

The most notable of positive psychology's predecessors, however, was the humanistic psychology movement, which originated in the 1950s and reached its peak in the '60s and '70s. This movement placed central emphasis on the uniquely personal aspects of human experience, including personal growth, **self-actualisation** (the realisation of one's own maximum potential and possibilities), hope, love and creativity. Humanistic psychologists were critical of disease-oriented approaches to a human being such as the biomedical model of mental health and believed that the so-called 'scientific method' (useful, in their view, for studying atoms, molecules and cellular processes) helped little in understanding the real complexity of the human condition. This area of psychology called for research focused more at the subjective, qualitative level rather than at the objective, quantitative level, and this is where positive psychology disagrees with its major predecessor. Contrary to the humanistic psychologists, whilst rejecting the mainstream psychology preoccupation with negative topics, positive psychology embraces the scientific paradigm. Positive psychology thus distinguishes itself from humanistic psychology on the basis of its methods, presenting itself, rightly or wrongly, as a new movement attempting, at times, to distance itself from its origins.

4.1.3 The scope of positive psychology

The science of positive psychology, then, operates on three different levels. These are the level of emotions, the level of individual characteristics and traits, and the level of the group or institution.

The emotional level includes the study of positive experiences such as the positive emotions (Box 4.1) of joy, contentment and hope, and also well-being and flow. **Flow** is a state of optimal engagement. When this state is experienced, involvement in an activity is so great that one completely forgets about time and becomes unaware of the world outside. Many activities are conducive for flow, such as sports (Figure 4.3), dancing, solving a difficult puzzle, or a lively intellectual discussion.

Figure 4.3 A runner focusing on reaching the finish line, absorbed completely in the challenge of the race, can be said to experience a state of flow.

Mihaly Csikszentmihalyi (1975) was the first researcher to identify and name flow states as such. The state of flow happens under very specific conditions. For example, when we encounter a challenge that is testing for our skills, and yet our skills and capacities are such that it is just about possible to meet this challenge, then we experience a state of flow. So both the challenge and the skills are at high levels, stretching us almost to the limit. If challenges exceed skills, one can become anxious. If skills exceed challenges, one can become bored (like bright kids at school). Neither of these two cases results in flow. This particular level within positive psychology is therefore about feeling good, rather than doing good or being a good person and is also referred to as the 'level of positive affect'.

Box 4.1 Positive emotions and their function

Positive emotions, such as compassion, hope, joy, interest, awe and contentment, have long been a forgotten cousin of the powerful negative emotions that have attracted plenty of attention in the field of psychology. Using experimental methodologies, Barbara Fredrickson has demonstrated that positive emotions have very many important functions, such as:

- broadening our attention and thinking
- enhancing resilience
- building durable physical, intellectual, psychological and social resources
- initiating an upward developmental spiral.

For example, in one of her experiments Fredrickson showed participants various videos designed to elicit different emotions, ranging from amusement to anger (Fredrickson and Losada, 2005). After that, participants had to think of as many things as possible, that they would like to do right at that very moment. People induced to feel positive emotions (such as amusement) could think of more things to do than those induced to feel negative emotions (such as anger). This experiment therefore demonstrated the broadening of attention and thinking when experiencing a positive emotion.

'Future-mindedness' is a general orientation towards the pursuit and achievement of future goals.

At the next, individual level, the aim of positive psychology is to identify the constituents of the 'good life' and the personal characteristics and qualities that are necessary for being a 'good person', through studying our strengths and virtues, our future-mindedness, the capacity for love, courage, self-regulation, forgiveness, originality, wisdom, interpersonal skills and giftedness. Much of this level deals with **positive cognitions**, or positive ways of thinking and processing information about the world. Unfortunately though, one of the key contributions from the field of humanistic psychology (self-actualisation) is ignored here where it could be considered very relevant for this level.

■ What is self-actualisation?

□ The term 'self-actualisation' refers to achieving one's maximum potential.

The term 'civility' refers to courteous behaviour.

Finally, at the group, community and institutional level, the emphasis in positive psychology is on civic virtues, social responsibilities, nurturance, altruism, civility, tolerance, work ethics, positive therapy, positive business, positive education and other factors that contribute to the development of citizenship and communities and reaching beyond oneself.

As you can see, this level is much more about taking actions or positive behaviours aimed at something larger than ourselves.

4.2 The study of well-being

Positive psychology is usually referred to as 'the study of well-being'. Therefore the concept of well-being is the central phenomenon of its interest. Currently this field is flourishing, both in terms of increasing research output and in terms of public and political interest in the topic. But what does well-being actually mean?

4.2.1 What is understood under the notion of well-being?

Activity 4.1 Defining well-being

(LO 4.1) Allow 10 minutes

Pause for a few minutes now and consider how you might define well-being. What is it for you? Is it about feeling good? Is it about feeling contented? Could it be something to do with achieving what you really want in life? Write all your thoughts down before proceeding further. As you read through the next section, compare your own definition with the one achieved through the study of positive psychology.

One of the factors connected to the term well-being is happiness (Figure 4.4).

Within positive psychology literature, the term subjective well-being (or SWB; Book 1, Section 1.1.2) is also used and taken to be entirely synonymous with happiness. However, SWB is not only about how we feel. It is also about how we perceive our lives:

SWB = life satisfaction + affect

The first (cognitive) part of SWB is expressed by the term **life satisfaction**. Life satisfaction represents one's assessment of one's own life. One is satisfied when there is little or no discrepancy between the present and what is thought to be an ideal or deserved situation. On the other hand, dissatisfaction is a result of a substantial discrepancy between present conditions and the ideal standard. Dissatisfaction can also be a result of comparing oneself with others (see Section 1.2.1).

Figure 4.4 One of the key tasks for psychology is to define clearly mental states such as happiness in a way that they can then be measured and subject to research.

Affect, on the other hand, represents the emotional side of SWB. The notion of affect comprises both positive and negative moods and emotions that are associated with our everyday experiences. Emotions are our subjective experiences that are short-lived and often fleeting, whilst moods are relatively long-lasting subjective states. Note, though, that the term 'happiness' is not considered at this level within positive psychology, i.e. in the affective part of the well-being equation. Instead, as mentioned above, it is a term that is synonymous with, and used interchangeably with, SWB. Both the cognitive and affective components of subjective well-being are shown in Figure 4.5.

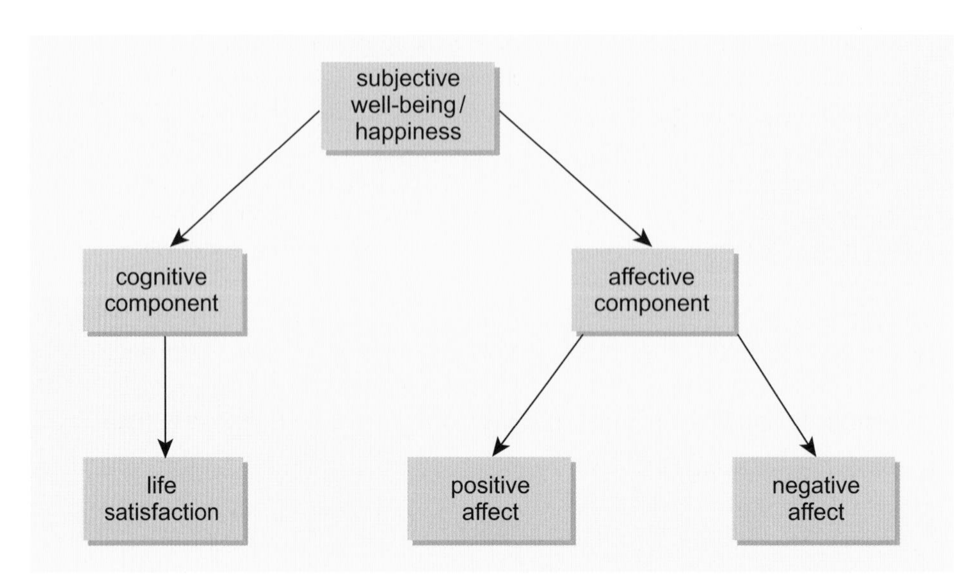

Figure 4.5 Affective and cognitive components of subjective well-being (SWB).

Looking back at the exemplars of well-being introduced in Book 1, Chapter 1, we find that all three individuals appear to be satisfied with their lives, experience positive emotions and have few, if any, negative emotions. Ho, a schoolteacher (Figure 4.6), draws satisfaction from his work and is very absorbed in his activities (likely experiencing a sense of flow). Claudia, a farmer, derives her positive emotions from enjoying her work and close relationships. Although she has 'considerable stress', it appears that her life has more positive than negative emotions. Finally, Henry, a gardener, hardly ever feels unhappy, and is referring instead to experiencing wonder, curiosity, calmness and a 'high'.

Figure 4.6 Ho, introduced in Book 1, Chapter 1, can be said to experience a state of flow from his teaching activities.

4.2.2 Measuring well-being: objective vs subjective assessment

So how do we know whether someone is feeling psychologically well or not? A famous Dutch researcher, Ruut Veenhoven (1991), has argued that well-being cannot be measured objectively (hence the adoption of the term *subjective* well-being amongst positive psychologists) because no overt behaviours are linked to it in a reliable manner. For example, an outgoing and friendly appearance, which can be frequently observed among happy people, can also be present in unhappy people, who, for one reason or another, may be motivated to hide their dissatisfaction with life and their unhappiness. For Veenhoven, therefore, directly asking a person about their well-being is the only way to access this information. You may, however, have your own thoughts as to whether this method of measuring well-being can also be subject to a person's motivations to hide their dissatisfaction and unhappiness.

Nobel Prize winner, psychologist Daniel Kahneman (1999), on the other hand, expresses dissatisfaction with the concept of SWB. He points out that when we are asked to evaluate our life as a whole, we may or may not be able to recall immediately some of the events that might need to be taken into account, becoming victims of our memory biases. This may be particularly true for individuals who are experiencing a state of depression, caught up in a cycle of negative thinking (Book 1, Section 1.3.1). Instead, Kahneman argues for an objective assessment of well-being, which he suggests could be derived by averaging multiple records of life experiences over a period of time (see Box 4.2).

Box 4.2 Research Methods: Experience sampling method

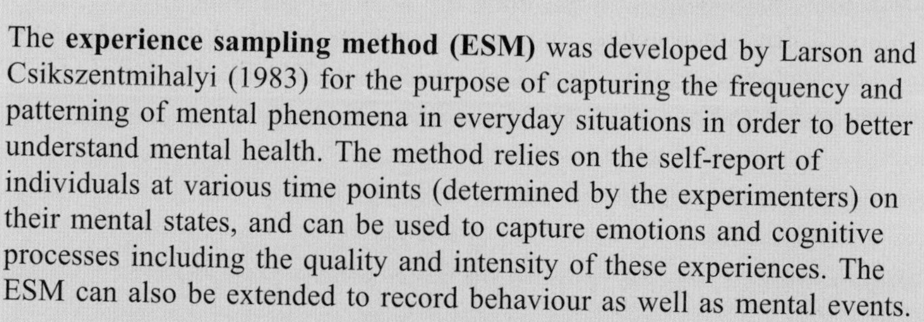

The **experience sampling method (ESM)** was developed by Larson and Csikszentmihalyi (1983) for the purpose of capturing the frequency and patterning of mental phenomena in everyday situations in order to better understand mental health. The method relies on the self-report of individuals at various time points (determined by the experimenters) on their mental states, and can be used to capture emotions and cognitive processes including the quality and intensity of these experiences. The ESM can also be extended to record behaviour as well as mental events.

Recording can be done on study-specific rating scales or on blank pages in order to capture fully the quality of the experience. Use of ESM in a study therefore provides subjective evidence of mental phenomena and behaviour as the technique is totally reliant on an individual's ability to self-report. However, ESM can provide both qualitative and quantitative data. Qualitative data might be in the form of a description of a momentary emotional experience, while quantitative data might come from the number of emotional experiences that occur during the ESM sampling period.

Using experience sampling methodology (Box 4.2) would allow us to collect multiple momentary accounts of well-being from research participants. This way, in Kahneman's opinion, well-being assessment does not need to be tied to memory and to retrospective accounts, and would not therefore be flooded with memory-reliant evaluations.

> A [...] task is to develop methods that minimize the biases of retrospective assessments in order to achieve a measurement of objective happiness that is at once valid and efficient.
>
> *(Kahneman, 1999, p. 22)*

We can question, however, whether Kahneman's proposal for measuring well-being is truly objective, as it relies still on the subjective judgement of individuals.

Figure 4.7 Could such an approach be the only method of validly capturing the mental phenomenon of well-being?

In fact, both the SWB equation and ESM rely on asking people about their well-being (Figure 4.7). One can argue that a truly objective measure of well-being would avoid any such subjective accounts, relying only on independent biological or neuropsychological assessment. However, it is difficult to see how this approach could work without any form of self-reported confirmation of the state of well-being.

Whilst it is not yet possible to study our cognitive evaluations of well-being (life satisfaction) using imaging technologies, considerable advances have been made in our understanding of brain mechanisms that underlie our affective style. For example, using functional magnetic resonance imaging (fMRI; Box 4.3) in a series of studies, Davidson (2005) investigated which areas of the brain are active at the time of processing different types of stimuli. These studies have demonstrated that positive affect is processed in the left prefrontal cortex, an area that is rich in dopamine receptors and essential to cognitive processing and flexibility. Negative affect is processed in the right prefrontal cortex (see Book 1, Section 2.2.2 for more information on Davidson's studies).

Box 4.3 Functional magnetic resonance imaging

Functional magnetic resonance imaging (fMRI) is one of two types of magnetic resonance imaging (the other being structural) which relies on the use of magnetic fields to measure activity in the brain. This measurement is possible because when parts of the body, including the brain, are exposed to a strong magnetic field the particles or atoms that make up the body are disturbed by the magnetic field. This disturbance causes the atoms to resonate, a bit like a tuning fork 'singing' when it is tapped. Different atoms are said to have different magnetic resonances – they sing different notes. After a brief period the atoms will return to their normal state and as they do so, they give out energy, dependent on their magnetic resonance, which can be detected by sensors around the participant's head.

fMRI scans use the principle of magnetic resonance to study blood flow. Crucially a particular component of blood, called haemoglobin, the molecule that makes blood red, comes in two different forms which have different magnetic resonances. Haemoglobin with oxygen attached is called oxyhaemoglobin, whilst haemoglobin that has no oxygen attached to it is called deoxyhaemoglobin. When particular regions of the brain become more active, they use more oxygen. Blood is diverted to these regions and the oxygen is removed from the oxyhaemoglobin, producing deoxyhaemoglobin. This change can be detected by the sensors.

Computer wizardry effectively subtracts the images produced when the participant is *not* performing the task from the images produced when the participant *is* performing the task. What remains is a composite image showing the difference in blood flow between when the participant was and was not performing the task. The difference in blood flow is usually represented as a colour scale on images and is assumed to indicate where the brain carries out the particular function (Figure 4.8).

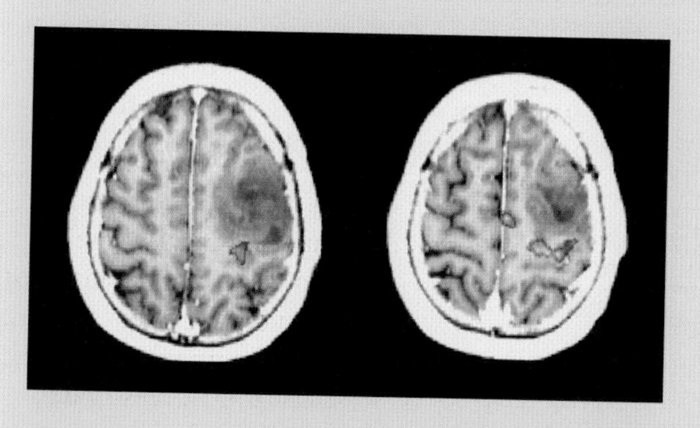

Figure 4.8 Two fMRI images taken at different horizontal levels in the brain whilst a participant finger-tapped with the left hand. The front of the brain is towards the top of the figure. The orange colour in the right hemisphere indicates the regions of increased blood flow as a result of increased activity.

fMRI scanners are noisy and the person is confined in a small space, having to use mirrors to see out of the scanner, and has to remain very still. The noise, constriction and motionlessness make for an uncomfortable experience.

In fact, most researchers would agree that different kinds of methods and analyses can supplement each other, so the best assessment of well-being would most likely combine neuropsychological tools with both global and momentary self-report survey measures, supporting the contention made throughout SDK228 that both subjective and objective accounts of mental phenomena are required to obtain a full understanding. However, given the costs associated with neuroimaging, surveys remain the main method used by positive psychologists for the purpose of studying well-being.

4.2.3 Subjective assessment of well-being

Early self-report assessments used for measuring well-being were single-item measures that, somewhat surprisingly, possessed a degree of construct validity (Diener et al., 2002).

- ■ Why should a test have construct validity?
- □ Validity is an essential concept in psychology and, when referring to tests such as self-report measures, it means that the test measures the mental phenomenon that it was designed to measure (Book 1, Section 4.2.4).

- ■ Why might it be surprising that a single instrument could validly assess well-being?
- □ If we follow the SWB equation given previously, well-being is a multidimensional construct that has both cognitive and affective components. One might therefore think that well-being scales need to capture accurately both of these components in order to capture fully all aspects of well-being.

The most commonly used measure of life satisfaction, at present, is the 'Satisfaction With Life Scale' (SWLS) constructed by Diener et al. (1985). The SWLS asks its respondents to judge how far they agree or disagree with the following five statements. They are asked to use a 7-point rating scale, ranging from (1) strongly disagree to (7) strongly agree, and with (4) being the neutral ground (neither agree nor disagree):

- 'In most ways my life is close to my ideal.
- The conditions of my life are excellent.
- I am satisfied with my life.
- So far I have gotten the important things I want in life.
- If I could live my life over, I would change almost nothing.'

(Diener et al., 1985)

Another well-known measure of the cognitive side of SWB is the Subjective Happiness Scale (Lyubomirsky and Lepper, 1999). In the UK, the Revised Oxford Happiness Scale (Hills and Argyle, 2002) is also widely used, being significantly more detailed than many of its counterparts (i.e. the SWLS). Of interest, this particular scale was designed to measure happiness by including some items that were a complete reversal of items on the Beck Depression Inventory (Book 1, Box 4.9). However, contrary to what one might expect, positive affect is not simply the opposite of negative affect. Indeed, Tellegen et al. (1988) showed that positive affect correlates with negative affect at only −0.43.

- ■ Why does a correlation of −0.43 show that positive affect is not simply the opposite of negative affect?
- □ If positive affect was exactly the opposite of negative affect, a correlation of −1.0 would be expected (Book 1, Box 4.5).

Affect is studied experimentally, using procedures of mood induction (Box 4.4), through experience sampling methodology (Box 4.2) and via self-report scales. Early studies approached the emotional side of well-being as a balance between positive and negative affect (Bradburn, 1969) and a widely accepted method for measuring SWB involves summing life satisfaction and positive affect and subtracting negative affect from the total (Schmuck and Sheldon, 2001). A review by Lucas et al. (2003) identifies 11 widely used measures of affect, ranging from 1- to 300-item scales. The PANAS (Positive and Negative Affect Schedule) scales are the most frequently used measures of affect at present (Watson et al., 1988).

Box 4.4 The Velten mood induction technique

The Velten mood induction technique is one method of inducing a particular mood in experimental participants. The technique can induce a positive, negative or neutral mood. Mood induction can be used in positive psychology research, for example to discover the purpose of positive moods although there are many similar examples of mood induction statements on various internet self help, well-being sites. The technique involves reading and reflecting on various statements such as:

1 Today is neither better nor worse than any other day.
2 I do feel pretty good today, though.
3 I feel light-hearted.
4 This might turn out to have been one of my good days.
5 If your attitude is good, then things are good and my attitude is good.
6 I feel cheerful and lively.
7 I've certainly got energy and self-confidence to share.
8 On the whole, I have very little difficulty in thinking clearly.
9 My friends and family are pretty proud of me most of the time.
10 I'm in a good position to make a success of things.
11 For the rest of the day, I bet things will go really well.
12 I'm pleased that most people are so friendly to me.
13 My judgments about most things are sound.
14 The more I get into things, the easier they become for me.
15 I'm full of energy and ambition – I feel like I could go a long time without sleep.
16 This is one of those days when I can get things done with practically no effort at all.
17 My judgment is keen and precise today. Just let someone try to put something over me.
18 When I want to, I can make friends extremely easily.
19 If I set my mind to it, I can make things turn out fine.
20 I feel enthusiastic and confident now.

(Millard, 2009)

4.2.4 Correlates and determinants of well-being

So now we have clarified the factors of interest within positive psychology and how they are measured, what variables affect these factors –'well-being' and 'happiness' – and what does this tell us about mental health? What does and does not make us happy? Is it money, is it love, or is there something else of importance? This section will examine the evidence behind some major correlates and predicators of well-being that include personality factors, social relationships, work and employment, money, class, age, gender, education and religion. We will also consider a counter-intuitive lack of relationship between well-being and having children. Throughout this section, pay particular attention to whether the word 'correlate' is used, as the majority of the findings that we will go on to discuss now still rely on associations and are not able to tell us much about the direction of causality.

Personality factors and individual differences

One of the most significant correlates of happiness (subjective well-being) is **extraversion**, a stable personality tendency to seek and thrive on social contacts. This effect may be due to the tendency of extraverts to choose more social and physical leisure activities, to use more positive non-verbal expressions, and typically to exhibit socially enhancing behaviours. On the other hand, neuroticism, an enduring tendency to experience negative emotional states (Box 1.1), unsurprisingly has strong and pervasive associations with various measures of negative affect (DeNeve and Cooper, 1998). However, these are associations only, so we cannot say, for example, that being an extravert makes you happy.

Happy people tend also to be optimistic, to 'look on the bright side' (known as the 'Pollyanna' principle) (Argyle, 2001). Another correlate of happiness is explanatory style (Book 1, Section 3.5.3). Happy people interpret bad events as external (due to external factors), situational and unstable. On the other hand, they interpret positive events as internal, global and stable (Seligman, 2002). Diener et al. (1999) also demonstrate that self-esteem is another stable correlate of well-being, although a direction of causality in this relationship is similarly not yet determined.

Social relationships

Social relationships appear to be the greatest single cause of well-being (Argyle, 2001). Spending time with friends, for example, is associated with very high levels of positive affect (and indeed this may be what underlies the extraversion effect). Larson (1990) demonstrated that people feel happiest when they are with friends, followed by being with family and then being alone. However, only close and personal friendships appear to be of importance, not the number of friends or the mere process of socialising (Wheeler et al., 1983).

The state of being in love heads the list of correlates of positive emotions (Argyle, 2001). Diener and Seligman (2002) in their study of exceptionally happy people (upper 10% of 222 college students) found only one main difference between the happiest students and the rest of the students. The very happy people had a rich and fulfilling social life; that is, they spent the least time alone, had good relationships with friends and had a current romantic partner. While the positive affect associated with love usually declines over time (though it does not disappear), people in close personal relationships maintain a higher level of life satisfaction than those who are single, widowed, separated or divorced (Inglehart, 1990). Yet it is not merely the fact of being married that predicts happiness but also, unsurprisingly, the quality of the marriage (Russell and Well, 1994). The factors that seem to influence satisfaction with marriage include instrumental satisfaction (financial security and sharing of domestic tasks), emotional satisfaction (social support, intimacy and sex) and companionship in leisure. However, to add some complexity to these issues, research continually finds that heterosexual men are better off in a relationship, but heterosexual women seem to be better off single (Argyle, 1994). This study addressed heterosexual relationships; the same conclusions cannot be assumed for non-heterosexual relationships. This has been speculated to be the case because men get more emotional support when in a relationship whilst women get more when single, from friends for example (Figure 4.9a and 4.9b). Overall therefore, positive psychology research suggests that social circumstances play a very large role in maintaining well-being.

(a)

(b)

Figure 4.9 (a) Men may get more emotional support in a heterosexual relationship compared to being single. (b) Women on the other hand may derive more emotional support from their friends when single compared to when they are in a heterosexual relationship.

Families are the source of both positive and negative affect. Research findings on the effects of having children fluctuate from children having a zero effect on their parents' happiness to bringing the well-being of parents well down (Powdthavee, 2009; Veenhoven, 1994). Furthermore, having either young children under-five, or adolescent children, can lead to a decline in marital happiness (Twenge et al., 2003; Walker, 1977).

Work and employment

It is hardly surprising that satisfaction with work has been found to be related to satisfaction with life (Warr, 1999). Marie Jahoda (1982) argues that work provides people with five categories of experience essential for well-being: time structure, social contact, collective effort or purpose, social identity/status and regular activity. Interestingly, pay does not have a strong relationship with job satisfaction, but good relationships at work and work content do. The nature of the job, unsurprisingly, seems to have a strong relationship with overall well-being, according to Warr (1999). His model of employment proposes that some of the features of work (pay and physical conditions) increase well-being to a set point beyond which it can no longer be affected by these factors. Other features of work, such as the opportunity for control, skill use, job demand, variety, environmental clarity and opportunities for interpersonal contact, increase well-being up to a certain level, but too much of these can actually decrease well-being. Warr also demonstrates that greater employee well-being is significantly associated with better job performance, lower absenteeism and reduced probability of leaving an employer. Thus enhancing employee well-being is in the best interests of the employer.

Job satisfaction, however, can be adversely affected by role conflict, such as the conflicting demands of work and family. Role conflict is largely manifested in dual-career families and is especially detrimental for women who work over 25 hours a week and have young children (Haw, 1995).

Unemployment also has a strong negative effect on well-being, including on positive affect, negative affect and life satisfaction. Retirement, on the other hand, despite sharing some features with unemployment (such as the actual absence of employment), is associated with very different outcomes in terms of well-being. The well-being of the retired is, on average, greater than of those at work but, unsurprisingly, that differs depending on the nature of the previous employment (Argyle, 2001).

Money

Although the majority of people believe that money can buy happiness (or if all else fails, that a little more money would make them a little happier), the evidence for this wisdom is hardly overwhelming (as mentioned briefly in the example of pay above). Research into the relationship between income and life satisfaction finds, in general, rather low associations but they are statistically significant. Wealthy people are marginally happier than poor people, a difference that is considerably smaller than perhaps might be expected (Myers, 2000). Living in poverty does have an effect on well-being, most probably because the basic needs of people are not met in this circumstance. However, once these basic needs are satisfied, the difference between the poor and rich is negligible. Wealthy nations, though, do appear to be much happier than poorer ones (Figure 4.10) but this finding does not hold true for all nations (e.g. Venezuela) (Diener et al., 1999).

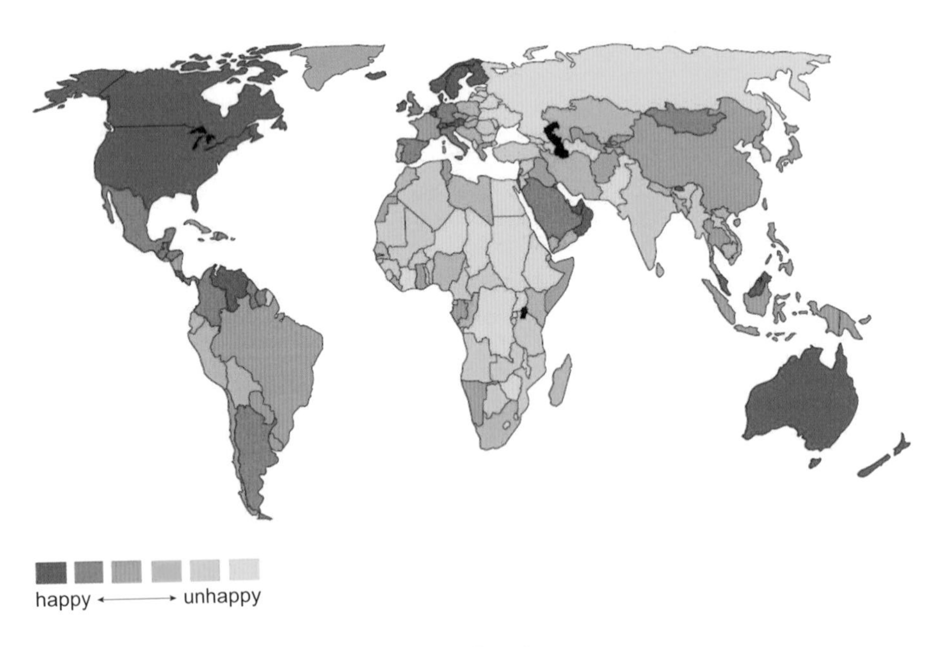

Figure 4.10 Mapping the well-being of nations.

The absolute or need theory states that income should be seen as a cause for happiness as it provides people with an instrument for fulfilling their needs. On the other hand, the relativity or comparison theory holds that the impact of income level depends on changeable standards and social comparisons (Diener et al., 1999). Thus, even the relatively affluent can feel poor in comparison with the very rich, especially taking into account the fact that habituation to an acquired level of income is fast (Csikszentmihalyi, 1992). Certainly the research supports the latter rather than the former theory.

Other demographic factors

Women and men report similar levels of well-being. However, their well-being is not equally counterbalanced in terms of the underlying factors: life satisfaction and affect. Although women experience more depression than men and report more negative affect, they also report more frequent and more intense experiences of positive affect and life satisfaction, thus arriving at a similar level of well-being overall compared to men (Diener et al., 1999).

A number of studies in the past have also suggested that there is a decline in well-being with age. However, recent research demonstrates that life satisfaction actually marginally increases rather than decreases with age (Diener et al., 1999).

The level of formal educational achievement has a very weak relationship with well-being, although it is stronger in poorer nations (Diener et al., 1999). It may be because, in poorer nations, education can make a substantial difference to one's earning potential or societal standing, whilst in the Western world a degree may not have such a dramatic influence on one's material affluence and social class. Qualitative studies would be particularly useful here to shed some more light on the nature of this relationship.

Figure 4.11 A strong relationship exists between religious devotion and well-being but most studies have been limited to Christian faiths.

A number of large-scale studies have shown significant correlations between well-being and religious certainty (Figure 4.11), the strength of one's relationship with the divine, prayer experiences, devotion and participation in religion. Religion appears to provide psychological and social benefits such as meaning in life, collective identity, social support and assistance in major life crises. There appears to be a better relationship between religion and life satisfaction than between religion and positive affect (Myers, 2000). One of the major drawbacks of these findings is that they are mainly based on studying a particular religious perspective, namely Christianity. It is currently unclear whether these conclusions can be generalised to other religions and traditions such as Buddhism or Islam, and especially to spiritual beliefs that are not embedded in a particular religious tradition.

The sustainable happiness model

The above research findings on the correlates and determinants of well-being, however, reflect short-term fluctuations in well-being and indeed other research has shown that individuals experience a relatively stable level of life satisfaction and affect across the different life domains in the long term (work, family, leisure). Genetic and personality predisposition theories argue that this element of consistency may be explained at the level of genes. Studies of identical twins reared separately show that approximately 50% of variation in emotionality can be ascribed to genetic variation (Tellegen et al., 1988). As we have seen, the levels of personality traits, notably extraversion and neuroticism, are also strongly and consistently predictive of well-being (Diener et al., 1999). Neuropsychological research also suggests that the relative level of prefrontal cortex activity is a stable trait over time (Davidson, 2005), providing a link between the levels of psychology and biology in well-being research.

Furthermore, researchers have found that individual circumstances, such as being married, employed, having money, etc., account for less than 5% of the variation in well-being levels, while a combination of life circumstances accounts for no more than 10% (Schwarz and Strack, 1991). The reason why life circumstances have such a small effect on well-being may well be because we adapt to most of them. Suh et al. (1996) explored well-being in a 2-year longitudinal study and found that only life events that occurred during the past 2–3 months influenced well-being. The **hedonic adaptation theory of life satisfaction** predicts that although happiness reacts to negative and positive life events, it returns to its baseline very shortly afterwards. Lottery winners soon return to their normal level of well-being and paraplegics and quadriplegics seem to adjust to their conditions and come back (at least very nearly) to their previous level of well-being (Seligman, 2002; Brickman et al., 1978). However, despite the evidence that people adjust to both lottery winning and injuries, there are certain conditions (such as widowhood, loneliness and injustice) that have been found to be much more difficult to adjust to (Seligman, 2002; Veenhoven, 1991).

Following a comprehensive review of the literature on the primary determinants of well-being, Lyubomirsky et al. (2005) created a model capturing the multiple influences on our well-being, called the **architecture of sustainable happiness**. In this model (which reflects very well a biopsychosocial approach) the set point is a genetically determined level of happiness, which remains relatively stable through the lifespan and returns to its original point quite soon after the majority of significant life events (there is hedonic adaptation). This set point accounts for variation in happiness up to approximately 50%. Life circumstances account for another 10% of the variation in well-being. These life circumstances include a person's national or cultural region, demographics, personal experiences and life status variables (e.g. marital status, education level, income, etc.). So what about the other 40%?

The remaining influence on well-being comes from **intentional activity** which refers to the committed and effortful practices a person can choose to engage in to enhance well-being. Significantly this intentional activity has the potential to counteract hedonic adaptation, offering a clear psychological pathway to chronic happiness and mental health improvement. This model therefore suggests the possibility of being able to change one's level of well-being beyond what is both biologically set, and determined by the life events that befall us (Figure 4.12). In the words of Lyubomirsky and colleagues:

> [the sustainable happiness model] implies that one's chronic happiness during a particular life period can be increased, but not by changing one's set point, because by definition it is constant. In other words, although it is possible that future scientists will learn how to alter people's basic temperaments and dispositions, at present it appears that focusing on the set point is not a fruitful avenue for happiness increase'.
>
> *(Lyubomirsky et al., 2005, p. 117)*

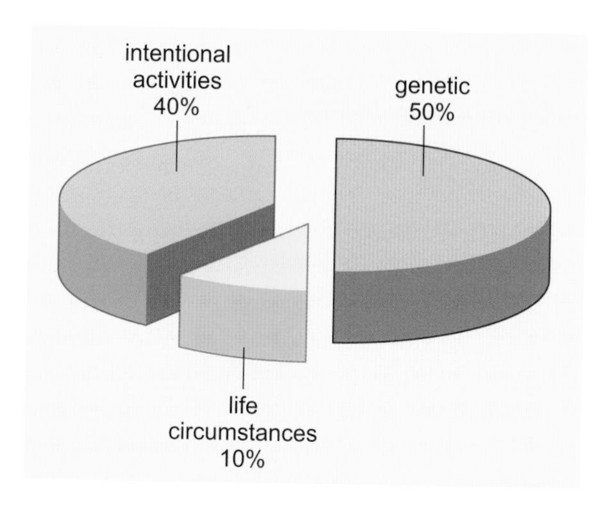

Figure 4.12 The sustainable happiness model predicts that it may be possible to intentionally change one's level of happiness in the long term through intentional activity that accounts for 40% of the variability in happiness.

The study of positive psychology thus carries a very powerful message. Whilst there is little point in negating or ignoring the circumstances that do befall us, it is important to realise that these circumstances are only a small part of the picture. Our well-being depends also on our own attitudes, and on the things that we choose to notice and take into account, on our intentions and on our deliberate practices. Let us now consider the activities, exercises and practices advocated by positive psychologists that can help us to change the way that we feel.

4.3 Positive psychology interventions

Accumulating evidence suggests that **positive interventions** involving intentional activities can be effective in either increasing or sustaining our level of well-being. A definition of what constitutes a 'positive intervention' is suggested by Sin and Lyubomirsky (2009, p. 467) to include 'treatment methods or intentional activities aimed at cultivating positive feelings, positive behaviors, or positive cognitions'. Seen as applicable to both clinical and non-clinical populations, positive interventions generally have been demonstrated to enhance well-being and reduce depression (Sin and Lyubomirsky, 2009).

In the past five years the field of positive psychology has made considerable progress in testing relatively simple positive interventions through randomised controlled trials (RCTs).

This section will therefore consider a range of these positive interventions, from forgiveness and optimism to using strengths and gratitude as well as the evidence for their effectiveness.

4.3.1 Forgiveness

Usually we think of forgiveness in terms of the victim altruistically excusing the wrong-doer, whose conscience is then eased. From this traditional perspective, the wrong-doer benefits but the victim gains nothing. Until relatively recently, forgiveness was considered strictly a religious matter, with most world faiths including some teachings and practices on the subject. But what if we take the perspective that forgiveness is something that we can also do for ourselves and not (only) for the person who has wronged us?

Researchers are beginning to examine the nature of forgiveness, and evidence is slowly emerging to support the contention that forgiveness is better for your well-being than going through life harbouring grudges and contemplating revenge. For example, research has shown that people who forgive are more likely to be happier, more agreeable and more serene (McCullough and Witvliet, 2002). Forgiveness is also linked to physical health benefits, such as a reduction in blood pressure, and it may aid cardiovascular recovery from stress (Friedberg et al., 2007). On the other hand, the study in Box 4.5 shows that nursing grudges or dwelling on revenge not only prevents you moving on, it also prompts higher levels of anger and sadness and a significantly higher heart rate and blood pressure (Witvliet et al., 2001).

Forgiveness may be difficult to achieve, for one may not be quite ready for it. But like any other habit, the more we practise it the easier it gets. A number of different forgiveness interventions have been validated to date (Lyubomirsky, 2008), including writing a letter of forgiveness (and then using judgement as to whether or not to send it), reading about various public figures who have practised forgiveness, forgiving oneself for a past transgression and imagining forgiving the wrong-doer.

Box 4.5 Evaluating the effects of forgiveness on well-being

In a within-participants study (Book 1, Box 3.1) conducted on 72 psychology students Witvliet and her colleagues (2001) instructed their participants to identify a person whom they blamed for mistreating them. Participants then had to imagine empathising with and forgiving this offender eight times (the forgiving condition), and also to remember the pain of being hurt and imagining harbouring a grudge towards this person eight times (the unforgiving condition). There were eight blocks of trials with each trial type presented once in a block in a counterbalanced order. Each block was followed by a relaxation trial with no imagery required. The whole experiment took place over 2 hours. The effect of the independent variable (forgiveness) was measured through self-reported ratings, on 20-point scales, of: arousal, anger, sadness, perceived control, and valence (this term refers to feeling overall negative or positive). The results are shown in Table 4.1. (*Note*: the empathy and forgiveness ratings were to check that the imagery conditions were successful in producing the psychological states that were intended.)

Table 4.1 Mean self-reported ratings (out of a total of 20) for the forgiving and unforgiving conditions in Witvliet et al. (2001). All of the measures were significantly different between the forgiving and unforgiving conditions.

Measure	Unforgiving	Forgiving
arousal	15.34	7.21
anger	15.75	5.11
sadness	11.71	7.14
control	8.37	13.03
valence	5.63	13.21
empathy	3.87	13.91
forgiveness	4.08	14.64

Overall, participants felt more negative during the unforgiving condition and experienced stronger negative emotions (anger and sadness) which, according to the SWB equation (Section 4.2.1), would lower their sense of well-being.

4.3.2 Optimism interventions

The notion of optimism can be related to different expectancies we may have about the achievement of goals, and other future events. **Optimists** have a generalised sense of confidence about the future, characterised by their broad expectancy that outcomes are likely to be positive. **Pessimists**, on the other hand, have a generalised sense of doubt and hesitancy, characterised by the future anticipation of negative outcomes. Although these terms seem similar to the notion of explanatory style first introduced in Book 1, Section 3.5.3, explanatory style relates specifically to how one interprets events that have already happened, while optimism and pessimism refer to the outlook one has on future events. The two are undoubtedly related however!

Research concurs that an optimistic attitude can signal very good news for both our mental and physical well-being (Carver and Scheier, 2002). Optimists tend to be happier than pessimists (Seligman, 2002) and, when dealing with difficult life events, optimistic people experience less distress, anxiety and depression than do pessimistic people. Optimists are also capable of learning something useful from negative events, persist longer at difficult tasks and tend not to give up, assuming that the situation can be handled successfully one way or another. Optimistic patients undergoing coronary bypass or breast cancer surgery experience less hostility and depression before surgery, and greater relief, happiness and satisfaction with medical care afterwards.

In one study of life insurance salespeople, it was found that the top 10% of optimists outsold the bottom 10% of pessimists by 88% (Seligman and Schulman, 1986). Contrary to popular belief, optimists don't necessarily wear rose-tinted spectacles either. There is evidence that 'glass half-full people' actually heed health warnings, rather than ignore them and hope the problem will go away. They also eat more healthily and tend to have more regular medical check-ups. However, a cautionary note should be sounded here (Section 1.3.3) as there is also evidence that optimism can be inappropriate in some circumstances, leading to rash decisions and risk-taking.

So can optimism be learnt? Apparently, yes. Although there may well be a genetically inherited component to optimism, and evidence suggests that early childhood experiences shape our optimistic–pessimistic traits, the field of positive psychology suggests that we can use several strategies to counter pessimism.

One of these is a **disputing strategy**, introduced by Martin Seligman (1991). We usually employ the skill of internal disputing when we are falsely accused of something by someone else. We think to ourselves, for example: 'That's not right. It's him who is not listening, it's not me. I always listen before reaching a conclusion'. However, when we falsely accuse ourselves of something (e.g. not being capable of dealing with a difficult situation) we don't tend to dispute it. The key to success is careful monitoring and recognition of our thoughts. Once a negative thought is detected, we can consciously dispute that thought and try to look at possible alternative outcomes.

4.3.3 Using strengths in a new way

Positive psychology defines **strengths** as relatively stable universal characteristics that capture what is best about people, i.e. the things that you are good at. But are strengths at all important? Surely, rather than boasting about what you are good at, you had better address your shortcomings. The initiators of the strengths movement within positive psychology argue from a very different position. They believe that two widespread assumptions about human nature are wrong. The first of them is that everyone can learn to be competent in almost anything. The second is that the greatest potential for growth is in the person's areas of greatest weakness. The argument instead is that our greatest capacity for growth and development lies within the areas of our strengths.

Activity 4.2 Personal strengths

(LOs 4.3, 4.4, 4.6) Allow 10 minutes

Take a few moments now to think about your own personal strengths. Make a list of those that you can think of within the space of 10 minutes.

The values in action (VIA) classification of character strengths (Box 4.6) lists the character strengths that have been identified as universal. Whilst the mere identification of our strengths has the potential to significantly increase well-being temporarily, a crucial ingredient for long-lasting well-being is using one's strengths in a new and different way. A randomised controlled trial by Seligman et al. (2005) established that using one's top five strengths for one week in a way that they have not been used before increased well-being and decreased depression for up to six months. If someone's strength is the love of learning, they may choose to spend a couple of hours researching a topic that always interested them in some way. If it is bravery, one may want to speak up for, or write about, an unpopular idea. Social intelligence may be used to make the day of one's customers, while kindness can also be applied to oneself. If the appreciation of beauty and excellence is someone's top or signature strength, they might enjoy spending their lunch hour visiting a museum. Incidentally, research demonstrates that a half-hour long museum visit dramatically reduces the level of the stress hormone cortisol in the body. A small-scale experiment run with 28 participants by Clow and Fredhoi (2006) showed that City of London workers with elevated levels of this hormone managed to achieve a dramatic reduction by visiting a gallery during their lunch-time break (Figure 4.13).

Although the study itself did not have a control group, a comparison with normal levels of cortisol for the time of the day, obtained from other studies, revealed that the cortisol levels of participants had dropped to below the normal range. Under normal circumstances during their working day, it would take participants about five hours to achieve such a level of decrease. As yet there is no research evidence as to whether such a reduction might have been achieved from a simple walk in the park, or whether the exposure to art was, in fact, the critical element.

Figure 4.13 What might underlie the reduction in cortisol seen in the study by Clow and Fredhoi (2006) Might it be the art itself or just the act of taking a break from work?

Using one's strengths in a new way may not be as straightforward as it sounds. (Think back to Activity 4.2. Did you find the first step of identifying your strengths easy or rather challenging?) Unless one's top strength is creativity, coming up with new ideas on ways to use one's strengths may also be quite difficult. After all, if you are already using your strengths, what else can you do with them? One may also wonder as to how this intervention is different from the laypersons's advice of 'do more of what you like'. Well, to the extent that what we like overlaps with our strengths, it may not be that different. However, research is yet to identify a 'strength' of television watching, the most common leisure time activity in the UK, that has been shown to have many negative effects (Boniwell, 2009).

Box 4.6 The values in action classification of character strengths

Positive psychology's values in action (VIA) classification of character strengths identifies 24 distinct strength characteristics that define what is best about people (Peterson and Seligman, 2004). These strengths are classified into six virtues that interestingly are the core universal characteristics emphasised by philosophers and religious leaders, suggesting that there may be a universal notion of what 'makes people good':

- Wisdom and knowledge – cognitive strengths related to the acquisition and use of knowledge (such as creativity and curiosity)
- Courage – emotional strengths involving the exercise of will to accomplish goals in the face of opposition, external or internal (such as bravery and honesty)
- Humanity – interpersonal strengths that involve tending and befriending others (such as kindness and capacity to love)
- Justice – civic strengths (such as teamwork and fairness)
- Temperance – strengths that buffer us against excesses (such as forgiveness and humility)
- Transcendence – strengths that connect us to the larger universe (such as humour and appreciation of beauty).

4.3.4 Gratitude interventions

Gratitude interventions are probably the most quoted of all positive psychology techniques and different variants of this exercise have been investigated by several researchers (Lyubomirsky, 2008; Seligman et al., 2005), always with significant results. The 'three good things' or 'counting one's blessings' exercise has been found to increase well-being and decrease depressive symptoms for up to six months (Seligman et al., 2005).

This technique instructs participants to look back at their day just before they go to bed and find three things that went well for them during the day or three things that they feel grateful for. An important part of the instructions relates to participants needing to reflect on their own role in these positive occurrences. It has been found that the timing of this exercise is important. Studies have shown that the well-being of those who carried it out three times a week for six weeks actually decreased slightly, which suggests that there is such a thing as too much gratitude intervention, whilst the well-being of those who carried out this exercise once a week for six weeks or every day for a week increased substantially. This finding coexists with the fact that people who continue to 'count their blessings' occasionally after the intervention demonstrate the best outcomes. The most likely conclusion is that it is important to notice the good things in life now and then, yet not to allow this practice to become a chore (Boehm and Lyubomirsky, 2009).

The above intervention is often contrasted with the so-called 'gratitude visit' which results in substantial but temporary increases in positive affect (Seligman et al., 2005). Its instructions state: 'Think of a person you feel grateful to for something that they have done for you in the past. Write a letter to them, describing what they did and what effect it had on you and your life. Once you have finished, give this person a ring and arrange an appointment to see them, preferably in their house. When you meet, read your letter out loud to the recipient'.

Boehm and Lyubomirsky (2009) explain the effects of gratitude by the fact that it promotes the savouring of positive experiences and does not allow people to take the positive aspects of their existence for granted, thus counteracting hedonic adaptation.

4.4 Using positive psychology interventions on a larger scale

Several group-based education and intervention programmes have been developed within the field of positive psychology (or closely related fields). This section will elaborate on two of these and will examine their evidence bases.

4.4.1 The Penn Resiliency Project

Several education programmes have been developed within the field of positive psychology in recent years, some aiming to prevent the development of future mental health problems, others aiming to enhance the skills of well-being directly.

One of the most notable educational interventions is the Penn Resiliency Project (PRP). This is a schools-based curriculum designed to increase resilience and promote optimism, adaptive coping skills and effective problem-solving through the applications of cognitive behaviour therapy and learned optimism (Seligman, 1991) principles to normal populations.

- ■ What is resilience?
- □ Resilience is the ability to recover quickly from adverse events or stressful life changes (Section 3.2.1).

The PRP is delivered to 10–13-year-olds (Figure 4.14) in 12 sessions of 90–120 minutes, and educates them to challenge a habitual pessimistic explanatory style by looking at the evidence and considering what is realistic, whilst avoiding unrealistic optimism.

The PRP has been developed and researched for over 16 years, acquiring a solid base of evidence (Reivich and Shatté, 2003; Brunwasser et al., 2009). Out of the 13 randomised trials carried out with over 2000 participants, 11 of the studies have demonstrated reductions in depressive symptoms, with three studies also showing positive effects on anxiety and behavioural

Figure 4.14 The evidence for the efficacy of the positive intervention of the PRP is strong.

problems. At its best, the PRP has been proven to reduce the incidence of depression and anxiety by 50% at the three-year follow-up period (Gillham et al., 2007). Currently, trials are under way in the UK to establish the effects of the PRP not only on depression and anxiety, but also on well-being (using the Student Multidimensional Life Satisfaction Scale). Implemented in three local educational authorities, the PRP is delivered to 11-year-olds. Other, similar UK-developed pilots such as the Newham Resilience Initiative (NRI) are under way in London (Boniwell, 2009).

4.4.2 Quality of life therapy/coaching

Quality of life therapy/coaching (QOLTC) is a new approach to positive psychology intervention (Frisch, 2006). Clients are taught tools for boosting their satisfaction and fulfilment in any one of 16 specific areas of life (assessed by the Quality of Life Inventory) in order to enhance overall contentment or quality of life. These 16 areas include: goals and values, self-esteem, health, work, play, helping, learning, creativity, money, love, friends, children, relatives, home, neighbourhood, community. While QOLTC is aimed at non-clinical populations who wish to be happier and more successful, it also aims to teach clinicians how to integrate positive psychology into their clinical practice.

In QOLTC the therapist or a coach works with the client to select two to five areas of life from the inventory that are seen by the client as highly essential for his or her well-being, but which have high levels of dissatisfaction. In subsequent sessions, cognitive behaviour strategies are used to facilitate changes in the attitudes or perceptions of this area. These strategies include (but are not limited to) the following: expressive writing, relaxation, meditation, daily stress diaries, problem-solving, volunteering, creating a 'playlist' (identification of a wide range of mood-enhancing activities), worry management techniques, and goal-setting tools. The precise strategies chosen are specifically targeted to the areas needing improvement. In essence, clients are taught to put their time where their values are.

QOLTC has been evaluated as successful and superior to the standard treatment in randomised controlled trials (Rodrigue et al., 2005; Rodrigue et al., 2006). In one of the trials (Rodrigue et al., 2005), using the QOLTC with wait-listed lung transplant patients led to significant improvement in quality of life, mood, and social intimacy. Furthermore, improvements in quality of life and mood appear to be maintained for as long as three months after treatment.

4.4.3 Mindfulness meditation

Mindfulness, otherwise defined as a receptive attention to, and awareness of, present events and experience (Section 3.3.1), is one of the major interventions promoted by positive psychology. It is also a practice that has been around for many thousands of years, as a common element of Eastern religions, and is typically associated with Buddhism. It entails the skills of paying attention purposefully, in the present moment and without judgement (Box 4.7).

Box 4.7 The experience of mindfulness

Mindfulness is a form of self-awareness training that has been adapted from Buddhist mindfulness meditation. Mindfulness can be utilised in many situations (e.g. while cleaning, walking or queuing) but it does require practice. Practising the technique of mindfulness while walking might involve the following as an example:

While walking, concentrate on the feel of the ground underneath your feet, and on your breathing. Just observe what is around you as you walk, staying in the present. Let your other thoughts go, just look at the sky, the view, the other walkers; feel the wind, the temperature on your skin; enjoy the moment.

Mindfulness therefore involves effortless concentration and full attentiveness to what is being experienced at a particular moment. The idea is to simply allow oneself to be absorbed in the here and now, rather than being mentally transported elsewhere. This can enhance the sense of presence (and by doing so, the sense of being alive) and usually has a calming effect.

Activity 4.3 Mindfulness meditation and effects on well-being

(LOs 4.4, 4.6) Allow 20 minutes

Now would be an ideal time to go to the multimedia map and watch the video and audio clips on mindfulness meditation. Then follow the instructions in the activity.

Neuropsychological studies demonstrate that mindfulness meditation produces changes in brain activation associated with reductions in negative affect and increases in positive affect. They also reveal a clear link between meditation and immune function, and between changes in brain function and immunity among meditators. For instance, participants in an 8-week-long meditation course were compared with participants on a waiting list in terms of brain and immune system activity. It was found that those in the meditation course showed increased left-hemisphere activity (associated with positive emotions) as well as increased production of antibodies in response to an influenza vaccine (see Davidson et al., 2003, whose work was introduced in Book 1, Section 2.2 and referred to again earlier in this chapter). Both trait (a personality predisposition) and state (the actual experience of mindfulness) (Box 1.2) are predictors of different aspects of affective well-being (Brown and Ryan, 2003). The meta-analysis of the effects of mindfulness meditation intervention across 20 controlled and 27 observational studies concluded that it is also an effective intervention for a range of chronic diseases in a variety of samples (Grossman et al., 2004). Unfortunately, though, the majority of these studies suffer from small sample sizes. Further studies with larger sample sizes may throw more light on the value of this type of intervention.

4.5 Is positive psychology here to stay?

Despite being a relatively young discipline, the study of positive psychology is gaining in popularity. The key question, however, is whether positive psychology tells us anything that we didn't already know. For example, Argyle (2001) argues that it doesn't really need to be proved that people want to be happy. In this vein, some findings from positive psychology research are rather uninspiring: it also doesn't need to be proved that being divorced or being unemployed makes people unhappy.

The scientific study of well-being does, however, offer some valuable insight into warding off mental distress in the form of negative emotions, and in guarding against the development of mental health problems. There have also been some findings from positive psychology research that were very surprising. For example, contrary to popular belief, money does not make people happy. In addition, the overwhelming relationship between sociability and happiness had been previously unknown. Positive psychology's most salient finding, however, is that happiness is partly innate (e.g. the sustainable happiness model), but it can also be changed. As much as a 40% fluctuation may be possible through one's intentional activities and these activities can counteract hedonic adaptation and the genetic set-point on the happiness scale.

4.5.1 Positive psychology with a pinch of salt

A lack of an acknowledgement of its historical roots

Although positive psychology has a very rich history with many predecessors, it is often surprisingly ignorant of previous developments in the study of well-being and happiness (many of which are thousands of years old). Not only can this lead to reinventing the wheel, but also to staking a claim to someone else's ideas without adequate acknowledgement. Luckily, some positive psychologists agree that acknowledgements are very important, and recognise that better connections with its historic roots would make positive psychology stronger, rather than weaker. Attempting to argue that the movement is brand new only leaves an impression of innovation, which disappears if one opens any reference book on an entry for 'happiness'.

Reductionist 'scientific' methodology

It is not the first time psychology has attempted to model the study of a person on the natural sciences. Many psychologists, although they are probably still in the minority, wonder how such a complex subject as the human being can be studied by a methodology that reduces it to numbers and statistics. Two of the major problems with adopting such an approach lie in either elaborating the obvious (something that your grandmother knew) or failing to address any important questions.

Drawing big conclusions out of weak findings

Even when adopting the mainstream 'scientific' ideology, positive psychology often relies on methods that are cheaper and easier to run. More than half of the studies in the field are so-called correlational studies. Correlational studies (introduced in Book 1, Section 4.2.5) help to establish that one thing is reliably associated with another (e.g. exercising is associated with better health). However, correlational studies do not allow us to conclude that one thing leads to another. For example, people who exercise might be healthier because of their exercise habit, or people who are healthier might have more energy to engage in exercise. Even though psychologists know very well that correlations do not imply causality, they sometimes interpret the finding as if they did.

Danger of becoming an ideological movement

'Hooray for positive psychology!' 'Make sure to get on the bandwagon!' These are the types of implicit slogans that prompted several thinkers to assert that positive psychology may be in danger of becoming an ideological movement. Amongst the many hazards of that are the narrow mind-set, resenting any criticism, hero worship, self-perpetuating beliefs, arrogance and getting stuck in self-imposed positivity, leading to a lack of depth, lack of realism and simplifications.

One example of such simplification is the location of responsibility for well-being firmly within the individual, with a side effect that victims of unfortunate circumstances and other sufferers can be blamed for their own misery. This viewpoint completely ignores the social aspect of the biopsychosocial model. In this way, the tyranny of the positive attitude may paradoxically reduce subjective well-being, the very condition it is designed to enhance (Held, 2004).

One-sidedness and lack of balance

Even if one succeeded in engaging in positive thinking and feelings, not paying much attention to the stressful sides of life, would that really guarantee happiness? Or, perhaps, boredom? A well-known existential psychotherapist Emmy Van Deurzen (2008) is apprehensive about paying too much attention to positive interventions, arguing that by artificially suppressing the pain and fear, we may, paradoxically, help them grow even stronger. The late Richard Lazarus (2003, p. 94) challenged the implicit message of separation between the positive and negative, arguing that they are just two sides of the same coin: 'Speaking metaphorically, rather than mystically, God needs Satan and vice versa. One would not exist without the other. We need the bad, which is part of life, to fully appreciate the good. Any time you narrow the focus of attention too much to one side or another, you are in danger of losing perspective'. Realities of life most often fall in between the positive and negative, often making it hard to separate positive emotions from the negative ones or genetic determinants from one's own free will. If the psychology of the past made a major mistake of focusing mainly on the negative, often at the expense of the positive, isn't positive psychology making the same mistake by allowing the pendulum to swing to the opposite side (Figure 4.15)?

Figure 4.15 Might the positive nature of positive psychology be equally as unbalanced as the negative focus of 'psychology as usual'?

4.5.2 The future

Although it is hard to predict the future, there seem to be three major potential trajectories for the science of positive psychology. On the one hand, positive psychology may continue as it is at present as a distinct movement, focused on the positive with the help of scientific methods, attracting substantial interest. On the other hand, in accordance with the concerns of its sceptics, it may turn out to be a fad, failing to discover anything of major significance and falling victim to its own ideology. In the third possible trajectory, however, positive psychology may reach a point of synthesis with 'psychology as usual' and its rich heritage, embracing the diversity of available methods, integrating the positive with the negative and amalgamating all that we do and do not yet know about human beings. In this case, positive psychology might cease to exist as an independent movement, yet this would indeed be a result worth hoping for.

4.6 Final word

This chapter introduced the reader to the new discipline of positive psychology, focusing specifically on the study of well-being and attempts to increase well-being by means of interventions, delivered individually or in groups. We have briefly considered the complex influences on our well-being, life satisfaction and happiness, including the effects of genes and biology, and social and circumstantial factors. However, the emphasis in this chapter has been on our own psychological and intentional activities as a potential route towards enhancing mental well-being.

4.7 Summary of Chapter 4

- Positive psychology is the science of the positive aspects of human life, such as happiness and well-being.
- Positive psychology employs scientific methods in the study of well-being.
- Whilst positive psychology often presents itself as a new discipline, its roots can be traced back to Ancient Greek philosophers, Buddhism and humanistic psychology.
- The notion of subjective well-being is the currently dominant concept in positive psychology and it has both affective and cognitive components.
- Extraversion, neuroticism, social relationships, work satisfaction and religion are amongst the greatest circumstantial determinants of well-being, while money, age and having children have little (or sometimes a negative) effect on well-being.
- The sustainable happiness model postulates that genes account for up to 50% of variability in well-being, life circumstances for 10%, and intentional activity for 40%.
- The sustainable happiness model therefore postulates that it is possible to modify the set point of happiness in a long-term sustainable way that counteracts the process of hedonic adaptation.
- A positive intervention is an intentional activity that is positive at the point of application, in method, or both.

4.8 Learning outcomes

LO 4.1 Describe what is meant by the term subjective well-being within the field of positive psychology. (KU1, CS1)

LO 4.2 Recognise the need for different methods (subjective and objective) to obtain evidence for happiness and well-being levels, and recognise the factors that affect these. (KU1, KU3)

LO 4.3 Critically appraise the development, aims and approaches of the positive psychology movement. (KU1, KU3, KU5, CS3, CS4, CS5)

LO 4.4 Evaluate the evidence that it is possible to improve the well-being or happiness of people via specially devised training programmes. (KU3, KU4, CS4, CS5)

LO 4.5 Recognise the need for a holistic biopsychosocial perspective for understanding well-being. (KU3)

LO 4.6 Understand the theoretical basis for interventions aimed at improving well-being. (KU4)

4.9 Self-assessment questions

SAQ 4.1 (LO 4.3)

Why did positive psychology arise? What arguments were put forward by its pioneers to justify the establishment of this new discipline?

SAQ 4.2 (LO 4.2)

What is hedonic adaptation and how can it be overcome?

SAQ 4.3 (LOs 4.4 and 4.5)

Confucius wrote: 'Those who cannot forgive break the bridge over which they themselves must pass'. How does his wisdom correspond with recent research findings on forgiveness?

SAQ 4.4 (LO 4.6)

What is the common element of the two large-scale intervention programmes discussed in the chapter: the Penn Resiliency Project (PRP) and quality of life therapy/coaching (QOLTC)?

Answers and comments

Answers to SAQs

SAQ 1.1

(a) C; (b) E.

SAQ 1.2

No, they are not. Jean is unlikely to be diagnosed with MD because criterion B in Box 1.4 specifically excludes those whose symptoms may be linked to the loss of a loved one – which would appear to apply in her case. However, Bill would be diagnosed with MD, as job loss and consequent feelings of bereavement are not allowed for in the DSM-IV-TR criteria for MD.

SAQ 1.3

Yes, her case appears to satisfy criterion C. Suzanna has at least three of the symptoms listed, and she has suffered from GAD for over 6 months. The symptoms she has include: (6) sleep disturbance (she mentions insomnia); (5) muscle tension (she mentions 'feelings of tightness in the head') and (1) feeling keyed up or on edge (she mentions 'constant feeling that I am going to die', which could fit with this).

SAQ 1.4

The odds ratio that 'any anxiety disorder' will also be present in people who have major depression is 5.1. This means that the chance of 'any anxiety disorder' being present is 5.1 times higher in people who have major depression, compared to the normal chance of having 'any anxiety disorder'.

SAQ 1.5

The biopsychosocial model – because it recognises that underlying biology and psychosocial factors interact to produce the behaviour that we see.

SAQ 2.1

Yes, 'appraisal' – how you perceive events or situations, and how much control you feel you have over them, makes a difference to whether you feel stressed or not.

SAQ 2.2

Cortisol is produced by the adrenal cortex. It has an inhibitory effect on the pituitary gland and the hypothalamus. (*Note*: it also has an inhibitory effect on the hippocampus and the prefrontal cortex but these are not part of the HPA.)

SAQ 2.3

The weight of evidence suggests that both types of factors play a role. Combinations of genetic vulnerabilities and environmental factors may lead to the development of disorders. Environmental factors may also affect the sensitivity of systems such as the stress response system via changes in gene expression (epigenetic effects). Hence both genes and environment play a part in emotional disorders.

SAQ 2.4

Serotonin and noradrenalin. Their levels are lower in those who are depressed.

SAQ 2.5

As originally conceived, the monoamine hypothesis implied that simply raising the levels of monoamines such as serotonin would be sufficient to improve or correct mood disorders. SSRIs raise the levels of serotonin in the brain within hours, so the fact that mood improvement takes longer suggests that raising levels of monoamines is not, in itself, enough. Hence the problem – some other process or factor, not considered by the original monoamine hypothesis, must also be involved.

SAQ 3.1

(a) OCD is an anxiety disorder.

(b) Chronic anxiety disorders can be treated with SSRIs or SNRIs and cognitive therapy. In John's case he is being treated with the SSRI Prozac® (Book 1, Section 2.4.1) and brain lock (Book 1, Section 2.2.2).

SAQ 3.2

Although this is not a recommended treatment, the medication may improve the patients' mood, in part by working through the placebo effect (Book 1, Section 1.2.2). The patient could become more depressed if their expectations are not met and they feel they are not being taken seriously. The GP may not have long enough to make a proper assessment and this may give the opportunity to insist that the patient book another, longer appointment to allow assessment of their progress and monitoring of any side effects.

SAQ 3.3

Wearing and breathing through a gas mask for 5 minutes has the least good external validity. It is hard to think how this activity relates to an everyday activity in a modern urban environment.

SAQ 3.4

The characteristic that protects against psychopathology following a potentially traumatic event is resilience.

SAQ 4.1

Seligman and Csikszentmihalyi (2000) argued that after World War II the attention of researchers and practitioners in psychology shifted to the study of mental health problems in order to help those returning from the war. This resulted in an enhanced understanding and treatment of psychological disorders, leaving the study of normal lives and high talent somewhat under-researched.

SAQ 4.2

Hedonic adaptation is the tendency to remain at a relatively stable level of happiness despite a change in fortune or the achievement of major goals. According to this theory, as a person makes more money, or acquires a new position, then expectations and desires rise in parallel, resulting in no permanent gain in happiness. Intentional activities provide the means of overcoming hedonic adaptation, as we don't seem to adapt to them as quickly as we do to changes in circumstances.

SAQ 4.3

Research indicates that forgiveness has substantial psychological effects on the victim of a wrong-doing. Forgiveness reduces anger, sadness and arousal (stress) as shown by Witvliet et al. (2001) in Box 4.5.

SAQ 4.4

Both the PRP and QOLTC are based partly or fully on the principles of cognitive behaviour therapy.

Comments on activities

Activity 1.1

You may have thought of some of the following factors or come up with others:

- The GP is able to spend enough time with the patient to probe in a sensitive way and explore if there are any underlying issues (e.g. somatic or social) if the patient appears upset or worried.
- The GP is sensitive to emotional signals from the patient.
- The GP has specific mental health training.
- The GP knows of, and can apply, the biopsychosocial approach.
- The patient recognises, and is willing and able to speak about, his/her personal emotional distress.
- The GP is familiar with the patient (i.e. the patient is not a new, but is a regular visitor to the surgery) so is aware of what is normal or not for the patient.
- The GP has known the patient or patient's family for a while and knows the patient's medical issues.
- Having one of the patient's friends or family members present – they may be able to provide another perspective on the patient's condition.

Activity 3.2

Here are some things you may do when feeling low:

- run, exercise, go to the gym
- get out of doors: for a walk, with the dog, ride a horse, dig the garden, cut the hedge, slash some brambles
- cookery, especially baking
- shopping
- have a hot bath, stay in bed, eat chocolate, read a trashy novel, drink whisky
- play loud rock music, play uplifting classical music
- talk to partner, phone a friend.

Activity 4.1

Defining well-being may not be as easy as it seems as, quite often, well-being may be an experience that is unique to an individual. However, positive psychology attempts to reach a general definition of what well-being is that applies to all individuals across the board. You may wish to consider whether what makes you feel 'well' might also make others feel 'well'. Can such a global definition be reached and does it have something to do with happiness?

You will find out what positive psychology has to say on this matter as you read the rest of the chapter.

Activity 4.2

The majority of people are very reluctant to talk about their strengths and many do not even know what they are. So don't worry if you had trouble with this activity. Given the difficulties associated with individuals being aware of their own strengths, how viable might this be as a means of enhancing well-being? You should consider, for example, that optimists and those with a positive explanatory style might be better at doing this than those who are pessimists or those with a negative explanatory style. Consider, therefore, whether it might be very difficult to target this intervention at those who need it most.

References

Alloy, L.B. and Abramson, L.Y. (1979) 'Judgement of contingency in depressed and non-depressed students: sadder but wiser', *Journal of Experimental Psychology: General*, vol. 108, pp. 441–85.

American Psychiatric Association (APA) (2000) *Diagnostic and Statistical Manual of Mental Disorders*, 4th edn Text revision (DSM-IV-TR).

Anxiety UK (2007) [online], www.anxietyuk.org.uk/condition_gad.php (Accessed May 2010).

Arborelius, L., Owens, M.J., Plotsky, P.M. and Nemeroff, C.B. (1999) 'The role of corticotropin-releasing factor in depression and anxiety disorders', *Journal of Endocrinology*, vol. 160, pp. 1–12.

Argyle, M. (1994) *The Psychology of Social Class*, London, Routledge.

Argyle, M. (2001) *The Psychology of Happiness*, East Sussex, Routledge.

Aydemir, C., Yalcin, E.S., Aksaray, S., Kisa, C., Yildirim, S.G., Uzbay, T. and Goka, E. (2006) 'Brain-derived neurotrophic factor (BDNF) changes in the serum of depressed women', *Progress in Neuro-Psychopharmacology and Biological Psychiatry,* vol. 30, no. 7, pp. 1256–60.

Bear, M.F., Connors, B.W. and Paradiso, M.A. (2007) *Neuroscience: Exploring the Brain*, 3rd edn, Baltimore, Lippincott Williams & Wilkins.

Berton, O., McClung, C.A., DiLeone, R.J., Krishnan, V., Renthal, W., Russo, S.J. et al. (2006) 'Essential role of BDNF in the mesolimbic dopamine pathway in social defeat stress', *Science*, vol. 311, pp. 864–8.

Blazer, D.G., Hughes, D., George, L.K., Swartz, M. and Boyer, R. (1991) 'Generalized anxiety disorder', in Robins, L.N. and Reiger, D.A. (eds), *Psychiatric Disorders in America*, New York, Free Press, pp. 180–203.

Boehm, J.K. and Lyubomirsky, S. (2009) 'The promise of sustainable happiness', in Lopez, S.J. (ed.) *Handbook of Positive Psychology* (2nd edn), Oxford, Oxford University Press, pp. 667–77.

Bonanno, G.A. (2004) 'Loss, trauma, and human resilience: have we underestimated the human capacity to thrive after extremely aversive events?', *American Psychologist*, vol. 59, no. 1, pp. 20–8.

Bonanno, G.A. and Mancini, A.D. (2008) 'Human capacity to thrive in the face of potential trauma', *Pediatrics*. vol. 121, pp. 369–75.

Boniwell, I. (2009) *Time for Life: Satisfaction with Time Use and its Relationship with Subjective Well-being*, Saarbrucken, Germany, VDM.

Booij, L., Van der Does, B.C., Bremner, J.D., Cowen, P.J., Fava, M., Gillin, C. et al. (2002) 'Predictors of mood response to acute tryptophan depletion: a reanalysis', *Neuropsychopharmacology*, vol. 27, pp. 852–61.

Bowcott, O. (2010) 'Suicide rate on the rise, figures show', *The Guardian*, 28 January 2010 [online], www.guardian.co.uk/society/2010/jan/28/suicide-rate-on-rise (Accessed May 2010).

Bradburn, N. (1969) *The Structure of Psychological Well-being*, Chicago, Aldine.

Bredy, T.W., Zhang, T.Y., Grant, R.J., Diorio, J. and Meaney, M.J. (2004) 'Peripubertal environmental enrichment reverses the effects of maternal care on hippocampal development and glutamate receptor subunit expression', *European Journal of Neuroscience*, vol. 20, no. 5, pp. 1355–62.

Brickman, P., Coates, D. and Janoff-Bulman, R. (1978) 'Lottery winners and accident victims: is happiness relative?', *Journal of Personality and Social Psychology*, vol. 36, pp. 917–27.

Brown, G.W., Harris, T.O. and Hepworth, C. (1995) 'Loss, humiliation and entrapment among women developing depression: a patient and non-patient comparison', *Psychological Medicine*, vol. 25, pp. 7–21.

Brown, K. and Ryan, R. (2003) 'The benefits of being present: mindfulness and its role in psychological well-being', *Journal of Personality and Social Psychology*, vol. 84, pp. 822–48.

Browne, A. and Finkelhor, D. (1986) 'Impact of child sexual abuse: a review of the research', *Psychological Bulletin*, vol. 99, pp. 66–77.

Bruner, J.S. and Tagiuri, R. (1954) 'The perception of people', in Lindzey, G. (ed.) *Handbook of Social Psychology*, Reading, MA, Addison-Wesley, pp. 634–54.

Brunwasser, S.M., Gillham, J.E. and Kim, E.S. (2009) 'A meta-analytic review of the Penn Resiliency Program's effect on depressive symptoms', *Journal of Consulting and Clinical Psychology*, vol. 77, pp. 1042–54.

Campbell, S., Marriott, M., Nahmias, C. and MacQueen, G.M. (2004) 'Lower hippocampal volume in patients suffering from depression: a meta-analysis', *American Journal of Psychiatry*, vol. 161, pp. 598–607.

Carver, C.S. and Scheier, M.F. (2002) 'Optimism', in Snyder, C.R. and Lopez, S.J. (eds) *Handbook of Positive Psychology*, New York, Oxford University Press.

Caspi, A., Sugden, K., Moffitt, T.E., Taylor, A., Craig, I.W., Harrington, H., et al. (2003) 'Influence of life stress on depression: moderation by a polymorphism in the 5-HTT gene', *Science*, vol. 301, issue 5631, pp. 386–90.

Castre´n, E. (2005) 'Is mood chemistry?', *Nature Reviews Neuroscience*, vol. 6, pp. 241–6.

Chapman, T.F. (1997) 'The epidemiology of fears and phobias', in Davey, G.C.L (ed.) *Phobias: A Handbook of Theory, Research and Treatment*, Chichester, Wiley. Cited in G. Davey (2008) *Psychopathology: Research, Assessment and Treatment in Clinical Psychology*, Chichester, Wiley.

Chattarji, S. (2008) 'Stress-induced formation of new synapses in the amygdala', *Neuropsychopharmacology*, vol. 33, pp. 199–200.

Choy, Y., Fyer, A.J. and Lipsitz, J.D. (2007) 'Treatment of specific phobia in adults', *Clinical Psychology Review*, vol. 27, no. 3, pp. 266–86.

Clark, L.A., Watson, D. and Mineka, S. (1994) 'Temperament, personality, and the mood and anxiety disorders', *Journal of Abnormal Psychology*, vol. 103, pp. 103–16.

Clow, A. and Fredhoi, C. (2006) 'Normalisation of salivary cortisol levels and self-report stress by a brief lunchtime visit to an art gallery by London City workers', *Journal of Holistic Healthcare*, vol. 3, no. 2, pp. 29–32.

Compton 3rd, W.M, Helzer, J.E., Hwu, H.G., Yeh, E.K., McEvoy, L., Tipp, J.E. and Spitznagel, E.L. (1991) 'New methods in cross-cultural psychiatry: psychiatric illness in Taiwan and the United States', *American Journal of Psychiatry*, vol. 148, pp. 1697–704.

Csikszentmihalyi, M. (1975) *Beyond Boredom and Anxiety: Experiencing Flow in Work and Play*, San Francisco, Jossey-Bass.

Csikszentmihalyi, M. (1992) *Flow: The Psychology of Happiness*, London, Rider.

Darwin, C. (2009 [1872]) Cain, J. and Messenger, S. (eds) *Expression of Emotions in Man and Animals*, Penguin Classics.

Das-Munshi, J., Goldberg, D., Bebbington, P.E., Bhugra, D.K., Brugha, T.S., Dewey, M.E. et al. (2008) 'Public health significance of mixed anxiety and depression: beyond current classification', *The British Journal of Psychiatry*, vol. 192, pp. 171–7.

Davey, G.C.L. (1994) 'Worrying, social problem-solving abilities, and social problem-solving confidence', *Behaviour Research and Therapy*, vol. 32, pp. 327–30.

Davidson, R.J. (2005) 'Well-being and affective style: neural substrates and biobehavioural correlates', in Huppert, F.A., Baylis, N. and Keverne, B. (eds) *The Science of Well-being*, Oxford, Oxford University Press, pp. 107–39.

Davidson, R.J., Kabat-Zinn, J., Schumacher, J., Rosenkranz, M., Muller, D., Santorelli, S.F. et al. (2003) 'Alterations in brain and immune function produced by mindfulness meditation', *Psychosomatic Medicine*, vol. 65, pp. 564–70.

De Moor, M.H.M., Boomsma, D.I., Stubbe, J.H., Willemsen, G. and de Geus, E.J.C. (2008) 'Testing causality in the association between regular exercise and symptoms of anxiety and depression', *Archives of General Psychiatry*, vol. 65, no. 8, pp. 897–905.

DeNeve, K.M. and Cooper, H. (1998) 'The happy personality: a meta-analysis of 137 personality traits and subjective well-being', *Psychological Bulletin*, vol. 124, pp. 197–229.

DeRubeis, R.J., Siegle, G.J. and Hollon, S.D. (2008) 'Cognitive therapy versus medication for depression: treatment outcomes and neural mechanisms', *Nature Reviews Neuroscience*, vol. 9, pp. 788–96.

Dickerson, S.S. and Kemeny, M.E. (2004) 'Acute stressors and cortisol responses: a theoretical integration and synthesis of laboratory research', *Psychological Bulletin*, vol. 130, no. 3, pp. 355–91.

Diener, E. and Seligman, M.E.P. (2002) 'Very happy people', *Psychological Science*, vol. 13, pp. 81–4.

Diener, E., Emmons, R.A., Larsen, R.J. and Griffin, S. (1985) 'The satisfaction with life scale', *Journal of Personality Assessment*, vol. 49, pp. 71–5.

Diener, E., Lucas, R.E. and Oishi, S. (2002) 'Subjective well-being: the science of happiness and life satisfaction', in Snyder, C.R. and Lopez, S.J. (eds) *The Handbook of Positive Psychology*, New York, Oxford University Press, pp. 63–73.

Diener, E., Suh, E.M., Lucas, R.E. and Smith, H.L. (1999) 'Subjective well-being: three decades of progress', *Psychological Bulletin*, vol. 125, pp. 276–302.

Drevets, W.C. (1998) 'Functional neuroimaging studies of depression: the anatomy of melancholia', *Annual Review of Medicine*, vol. 49, pp. 341–61.

Drevets, W.C., Price, J.L., Simpson, J.R., Todd, R.D., Reich, T., Vannier, M. and Raichle, M.E. (1997) 'Subgenual prefrontal cortex abnormalities in mood disorders', *Nature*, vol. 386, pp. 824–7.

Duman. R.S. and Monteggia, L.M. (2006) 'A neurotrophic model for stress-related mood disorders', *Biological Psychiatry*, vol. 59, pp. 1116–27.

Duman, R.S., Malberg, J. and Thome, J. (1999) 'Neural plasticity to stress and antidepressant treatment', *Biological Psychiatry*, vol. 46, pp. 1181–91.

Duman, R.S., Heninger, G.R. and Nestler, E.J. (1997) 'A molecular and cellular theory of depression', *Archives of General Psychiatry*, vol. 54, no. 7, pp. 597–606.

Eaton, S.B., Konner, M. and Shostak, M. (1988) 'Stone agers in the fast lane: chronic degenerative diseases in evolutionary perspective', *American Journal of Medicine*, vol. 84, pp. 739–49.

Ekman, P. (1972) 'Universals and cultural differences in facial expressions of emotion', in Cole, J.R. (ed.) *Nebraska Symposium on Motivation 1971*, Lincoln, NE, University of Nebraska Press, pp. 207–83.

Ekman, P. (2003) *Emotions Revealed: Understanding Faces and Feelings*, London, Weidenfeld and Nicolson.

Emmons, R.A. (1996) 'Striving and feeling: personal goals and subjective well-being', in Gollwitzer, P.M. (ed.) *The Psychology of Action: Linking Cognition and Motivation to Behaviour*, New York, Guilford, pp. 313–37.

Forgas, J. (2009) 'Think negative! Can a bad mood make us think more clearly?', *Australasian Science (Nov-Dec 2009)*, pp. 14–17.

Fredrickson, B.L. and Losada, M.F. (2005) 'Positive affect and the complex dynamics of human flourishing', *American Psychologist*, vol. 60, pp. 678–86.

Friedberg, J.P., Suchday, S. and Shelov, D.V. (2007) 'The impact of forgiveness on cardiovascular reactivity and recovery', *International Journal of Psychophysiology*, vol. 65, no. 2, pp. 87–94.

Frisch, M.B. (2006) *Quality of Life Therapy: Applying a Life Satisfaction Approach to Positive Psychology and Cognitive Therapy*, Hoboken, New Jersey, Wiley.

Gilbert, P. (1989) *Human Nature and Suffering*, Hove, Erlbaum.

Gilbert, P. (1992) *Depression: The Evolution of Powerlessness*, Hove, Erlbaum; New York, Guilford.

Gillham, J.E., Reivich, K.J. and Freres, D.R. (2007) 'School-based prevention of depressive symptoms: a randomized controlled study of the effectiveness and specificity of the Penn Resiliency Program', *Journal of Consulting and Clinical Psychology*, vol. 75, no. 1, pp. 9–19.

Goldapple, K., Segal, Z., Garson, C., Lau, M., Bieling, P., Kennedy, S. and Mayburg, H. (2004) 'Modulation of cortical-limbic pathways in major depression: treatment specific effects of cognitive behaviour therapy', *Archives of General Psychiatry*, vol. 61, no. 1, pp. 34–41.

Grossman, P., Niemann, L., Schmidt, S. and Walach, H. (2004) 'Mindfulness-based stress reduction and health benefits: a meta-analysis', *Journal of Psychosomatic Research*, vol. 57, pp. 35–43.

Hall, F.S. (1998) 'Social deprivation of neonatal, adolescent, and adult rats has distinct neurochemical and behavioral consequences', *Critical Reviews in Neurobiology*, vol. 12, pp. 129–62.

Hammen, C., Brennan, P.A., Keenan-Miller, D., Hazel, N.A. and Najman, J.A. (2010) 'Chronic and acute stress, gender, and serotonin transporter gene–environment interactions predicting depression symptoms in youth', *Journal of Child Psychology and Psychiatry*, vol. 51, no. 2, pp. 180–7.

Haw, C.E. (1995) 'The family life cycle: a forgotten variable in the study of women's employment and well-being', *Psychological Medicine*, vol. 25, pp. 727–38.

Health Experience Research Group (2010) Interview 27 [online], University of Oxford, www.healthtalkonline.org/mental_health/Depression/People/Interview/896/Category/42/Clip/3565/ (Accessed May 2010).

Heim, C., Newport, D.J., Mletzko, T., Miller, A.H. and Nemeroff, C.B. (2008) 'The link between childhood trauma and depression: insights from HPA axis studies in humans', *Psychoneuroendocrinology*, vol. 33, pp. 693–710.

Heim, C., Newport, J., Heit, S., Graham, Y., Wilcox, M., Bonsall, R. et al. (2000) 'Pituitary-adrenal and autonomic responses to stress in women after sexual and physical abuse in childhood', *Journal of American Medical Association*, vol. 284, pp. 592–7.

Held, B.S. (2004) 'The negative side of positive psychology', *Journal of Humanistic Psychology*, vol. 44, no. 9, pp. 9–46.

Hills, P. and Argyle, M. (2002) 'The Oxford Happiness Questionnaire: a compact scale for the measurement of psychological well-being', *Personality and Individual Differences*, vol. 33, pp. 1073–82.

Hirschfeld, R. and Shea, T. (1992) 'Personality', in Paykel, E. (ed.) *Handbook of Affective Disorders*, New York, Guilford Press, pp. 185–94.

Hirschfeld, R.M.A. (2000) 'History and evolution of the monoamine hypothesis of depression', *Journal of Clinical Psychiatry*, vol. 61, suppl. 6, pp. 4–6.

Horwitz, A.V. and Wakefield, J.C. (2007) *The Loss of Sadness: How Psychiatry Transformed Normal Sorrow into Depressive Disorder*, New York, Oxford University Press.

Inglehart, R. (1990) *Culture Shift in Advanced Industrial Society*, Princeton, NJ, Princeton University Press.

Jahoda, M. (1958) *Current Concepts of Positive Mental Health*, New York, Basic Books.

Jahoda, M. (1982) *Employment and Unemployment: A Social Psychological Analysis*, Cambridge, Cambridge University Press.

Kahneman, D. (1999) 'Objective happiness', in Kahneman, D., Diener, E. and Schwarz, N. (eds) *Well-being: The Foundations of Hedonic Psychology*, New York, Russell Sage, pp. 3–25.

Kendler, K.S. and Prescott, C.A. (2006) *Genes, Environment and Psychopathology: Understanding the Causes of Psychiatric and Substance Use Disorders*, New York/London, Guilford Press.

Kendler, K.S., Gardner, C.O., Annas, P. and Lichtenstein, P. (2008) 'The development of fear from early adolescence to young adulthood: a multivariate study', *Physiological Medicine*, vol. 38, no. 12, pp. 1759–69.

Kendler, K.S., Hettema, J.M., Butera, F., Gardner, C.O. and Prescott, C.A. (2003) 'Life event dimensions of loss, humiliation, entrapment, and danger in the prediction of onsets of major depression and generalised anxiety', *Archives of General Psychiatry*, vol. 60, pp. 789–96.

Kendler, K.S., Karkowski, L.M. and Prescott, C.A. (1999) 'Causal relationship between stressful life events and the onset of major depression', *American Journal of Psychiatry*, vol. 156, pp. 837–41.

Kendler, K.S., Neale, M.C., Kessler, R.C., Heath, A.C. and Eaves, L.J. (1992) 'The genetic epidemiology of phobias in women: the interrelationship of agoraphobia, social phobia, situational phobia, and simple phobia', *Archives of General Psychiatry*, vol. 49, pp. 273–81.

Kessler, R.C., Ronald, C., Chiu, W.T., Demler, O. and Walters, E.E. (2005) 'Prevalence, severity, and comorbidity of 12-month DSM-IV disorders in the National Comorbidity Survey Replication', *Archives of General Psychiatry*, vol. 62, pp. 617–27.

Larson, R.W. (1990) 'The solitary side of life: an examination of the time people spend alone from childhood to old age', *Developmental Review*, vol. 10, pp. 155–83.

Larson, R.W. and Csikzentmihalyi, M. (1983) 'The experience sampling method', in Reis, H. (ed.) *New Directions for Naturalistic Methods in the Behavioral Sciences*, San Francisco, Jossey-Bass, pp. 41–56.

Lazarus, R.S. (2003) 'Does the positive psychology movement have legs?', *Psychological Inquiry*, vol. 14, pp. 93–109.

Lazarus, R.S. and Folkman, S. (1984) *Stress, Appraisal and Coping*, New York, Springer.

LeDoux, J.E. (1998) *The Emotional Brain: The Mysterious Underpinnings of Emotional Life*, New York, Touchstone.

Lee, J.L.C., Milton, A.L. and Everitt, B.J. (2006) 'Reconsolidation and extinction of conditioned fear: inhibition and potentiation', *Journal of Neuroscience*, vol. 26, no. 39, pp. 10051–6.

Levine, M. (2000) *The Positive Psychology of Buddhism and Yoga: Paths to a Mature Happiness*, New Jersey, Lawrence Erlbaum Associates Inc.

Levine, S. (1957) 'Infantile experience and resistance to physiological stress', *Science*, vol. 126, pp. 405–6.

Living Life to the Full [online], http://www.livinglifetothefull.com/index.php?section=page&page_seq=21 (accessed May 2010).

Lucas, R.E., Diener, E. and Larsen, R.J. (2003) 'Measuring positive emotions', in Lopez, S.J. and Snyder, C.R. (eds) *The Handbook of Positive Psychological Assessment*, Washington DC, American Psychological Association, pp. 201–18.

Lyubomirsky, S. (2008) *The How of Happiness: A Scientific Approach to Getting the Life You Want*, New York, Penguin Press.

Lyubomirsky, S. and Lepper, H.S. (1999) 'A measure of subjective happiness: preliminary reliability and construct validation', *Social Indicators Research*, vol. 46, pp. 137–55.

Lyubomirsky, S., Sheldon, K.M. and Schkade, D. (2005) 'Pursuing happiness: the architecture of sustainable change', *Review of General Psychology*, vol. 9, pp. 111–31.

Macdonald, W., Mead, N., Bower, P., Richards. D. and Lovell, K. (2007) 'A qualitative study of patient's perceptions of a 'minimal' psychological therapy', *International Journal of Social Psychiatry*, vol. 53, no. 1, pp. 23–35.

MacLean, P. (1990) *The Triune Brain in Evolution*, New York, Plenum Press.

Maddi, S.R. (2006) 'Hardiness: the courage to grow from stresses', *The Journal of Positive Psychology*, vol. 1, no. 3, pp. 160–8.

Maercker, A., Michael, T., Fehm, L., Becker, E.S. and Margraf, J. (2004) 'Age of traumatisation as a predictor of post-traumatic stress disorder or major depression in young women', *British Journal of Psychiatry*, vol. 184, pp. 482–7.

Malberg, J.E., Eisch, A.M., Nestler, E.J. and Duman, R.S. (2000) 'Chronic antidepressant treatment increases neurogenesis in adult rat hippocampus', *Journal of Neuroscience*, vol. 20, pp. 9104–10.

Mann, J.J. (2005) 'The medical management of depression', *The New England Journal of Medicine*, vol. 353, pp. 1819–34.

Marks, I.M. and Nesse, R.M. (1994) 'Fear and fitness: an evolutionary analysis of anxiety disorders', *Ethology and Sociobiology*, vol. 15, pp. 247–61.

Martinowich, K., Manji, H. and Lu, B. (2007) 'New insights into BDNF function in depression and anxiety', *Nature Neuroscience*, vol. 10, pp. 1089–93.

Matchett, G. and Davey, G.C.L. (1991) 'A test of a disease-avoidance model of animal phobias', *Behaviour Research and Therapy*, vol. 29, pp. 91–4.

Mayberg, H.S., Losano, A.M., Voon, V., McNeely, H.E., Seminowicz, D., Hamani, C., Schwalb, J.M. and Kennedy, S.H. (2005) 'Deep brain stimulation for treatment-resistant depression', *Neuron*, vol. 45, pp. 651–60.

McCaul, K.D., Mullens, A.B., Romanek, K.M., Erickson, S.C. and Gatheridge, B.J. (2007) 'The motivational effects of thinking and worrying about the effects of smoking cigarettes', *Cognition and Emotion*, vol. 21, no. 8, pp. 1780–98.

McCauley, J., Kern, D.E., Kolodner, K., Dill, L., Schroeder, A.F., DeChant, H.K., Ryden, J., Derogatis, L.R. and Bass, E.B. (1997) 'Clinical characteristics of women with a history of childhood abuse: unhealed wounds', *Journal of the American Medical Association*, vol. 277, pp. 1362–8.

McCrone, P., Dhanasiri, S., Patel, A., Knapp, M. and Lawton-Smith, S. (2007) *Paying the Price: The Cost of Mental Health Care in England to 2026*, London, King's Fund.

McCullough, M.E. and Witvliet, C.V. (2002) 'The psychology of forgiveness', in Snyder, C.R. and Lopez, S.J. (eds) *Handbook of Positive Psychology*, New York, Oxford University Press, pp. 446–58.

McGowan, P.O., Sasaki, A., D'Alessio, A.C., Dymov, S., Labonté, B., Szyf, M., Turecki, G. and Meaney, M.J. (2009) 'Epigenetic regulation of the glucocorticoid receptor in human brain associates with childhood abuse', *Nature Neuroscience*, vol. 12, pp. 342–8.

McManus, S., Meltzer, H., Brugha, T., Bebbington, P. and Jenkins, R. (eds) (2009) *Adult Psychiatric Morbidity in England, 2007: Results of a household survey* (APMS 2007) [online], The NHS Information Centre for health and social care, available from http://www.ic.nhs.uk/pubs/psychiatricmorbidity07 (Accessed May 2010).

Meaney, M.J. (2001) 'Maternal care, gene expression and the transmission of individual differences in stress reactivity across generations', *Annual Review of Neuroscience*, vol. 24, pp. 1161–92.

Melzer D., Tom, B.D.M., Brugha, T.S., Fryers, T. and Meltzer, H. (2002) 'Common mental disorder symptom counts in a population: are there distinct case groups above epidemiological cut offs?', *Psychological Medicine*, vol. 32, pp. 1195–201.

Millard, M. (2009) 'Velten Mood Induction' [online], http://www.wellbeingwizard.com (Accessed July 2010).

Mitchell, A.J., Vaze, A. and Rao, S. (2009) 'Clinical diagnosis of depression in primary care: a meta-analysis', *The Lancet*, vol. 374, pp. 609–19.

Mitra, R. and Sapolsky, R. (2008) 'Acute corticosterone treatment is sufficient to induce anxiety and amygdaloid dendritic hypertrophy', *Proceedings of the National Academy of Sciences USA*, vol. 105, pp. 5573–8.

Murray, C.L. and Lopez, A.D. (1996) *The Global Burden of Disease: A comprehensive assessment of mortality and disability from disease, injuries and risk factors in 1990 and projected to 2020*, Boston, Harvard University Press.

Myers, D.G. (2000) 'The funds, friends, and faith of happy people', *American Psychologist*, vol. 55, no. 1, pp. 56–67.

Nemeroff, C.B. (1998) 'The neurobiology of depression', *Scientific American*, vol. 278, no. 6, pp. 42–9.

Nesse, R.M. (2006) 'Evolutionary explanations for mood and mood disorders', in Stein, D.J., Kupfer, D.J. and Schatzberg, A.F. (eds) *American Psychiatric Publishing Textbook of Mood Disorders*, Washington DC, American Psychiatric Publishing. pp. 159–79.

NICE (National Institute for Health and Clinical Excellence) (2007) *Anxiety: management of anxiety (panic disorder, with or without agoraphobia, and generalised anxiety disorder) in adults in primary, secondary and community care* [online], http://guidance.nice.org.uk/CG22 (Accessed June 2010).

NICE (National Institute for Health and Clinical Excellence) (2009) *Depression: The Treatment and Management of Depression in Adults (Update)* [online], http://guidance.nice.org.uk/CG90 (Accessed May 2010).

Nitschke, J.B., Sarinopoulos, I., Oathes, D.J., Johnstone, T., Whalen, P.J., Davidson, R.J. and Kalin, N.H. (2009) 'Anticipatory activation in the amygdala and anterior cingulate in generalized anxiety disorder and prediction of treatment response', *American Journal of Psychiatry*, vol. 166, pp. 302–10.

Oatley, K. and Johnson-Laird, P.N. (1987) 'Towards a cognitive theory of emotions', *Cognition and Emotion*, vol. 1, pp. 207–33.

Ost, L.G., Alm, T., Brandberg, M. and Breitholtz, E. (2001) 'One vs five sessions of exposure and five sessions of cognitive therapy in the treatment of claustrophobia', *Behaviour Research and Therapy*, vol. 39, pp. 167–83.

Pagnin, D., de Queiroz, V., Pini, S. and Cassano, G.B. (2004) 'Efficacy of ECT in depression: a meta-analytic review', *Journal of ECT*, vol. 20, no. 1, pp. 13–20.

Paquette, V., Lévesque, J., Mensour, B., Leroux, J-M., Beaudoin, G., Bourgouin, P. and Beauregard, M. (2003) '"Change your mind and you change the brain": effects of cognitive-behavioral therapy on the neural correlates of spider phobia', *NeuroImage*, vol. 18, pp. 401–9.

Perry, B., Pollard, R., Blakley, T., Baker, W. and Vigilante, D. (1995) 'Childhood trauma, the neurobiology of adaptation, and "use-dependent" development of the brain: How states become traits', *Infant Mental Health Journal*, vol. 16, pp. 271–91.

Peterson, C. and Seligman, M.E.P. (2004) *Character Strengths and Virtues: A Handbook and Classification*, New York, Oxford University Press.

Poulton, R. and Menzies, R.G. (2002) 'Non-associative fear acquisition: a review of the evidence from retrospective and longitudinal research', *Behaviour Research and Therapy*, vol. 40, no. 2, pp. 129–49.

Powdthavee, N. (2009) 'Think having children will make you happy?', *The Psychologist*, vol. 22, no. 4, pp. 308–11.

Price, J.S. and Sloman, L. (1987) 'Depression as yielding behavior: an animal model based on Schjelderup-Ebbe's pecking order', *Ethology and Sociobiology*, vol. 8 (suppl.), pp. 85–98.

Proudfoot, J., Ryden, C., Everitt, B., Shapiro, D., Goldberg, D., Mann, A. et al. (2004) 'Clinical efficacy of computerised cognitive-behavioural therapy for anxiety and depression in primary care; randomised controlled trial', *British Journal of Psychiatry*, vol. 185, pp. 46–54.

Reivich, K. and Shatté, A. (2003) *The Resilience Factor: 7 Keys to Finding Your Inner Strength and Overcoming Life's Hurdles*, New York, Broadway Books.

Richardson, R., Ledgerwood, L. and Cranney, J. (2004) 'Facilitation of fear extinction by D-cycloserine: theoretical and clinical implications', *Learning and Memory*, vol. 11, pp. 510–16.

Risch, N., Herrell, R., Lehner, T., Liang, K.-Y., Eaves, L., Hoh, J. et al. (2009) 'Interaction between the transporter gene (5-HTTLPR), stressful life events, and risk of depression: a meta-analysis', *Journal of the American Medical Association*, vol. 301, pp. 2462–71.

Rodrigue, J.R., Baz, M.A., Widows, M.R. and Ehlers, S.L. (2005) 'A randomized evaluation of quality-of-life therapy with patients awaiting lung transplantation', *American Journal of Transplantation*, vol. 5, no. 10, pp. 2425–32.

Rodrigue, J.R., Widows, M.R. and Baz, M.A. (2006) 'Caregivers of patients awaiting lung transplantation: do they benefit when the patient is receiving psychological services?', *Progress in Transplantation*, vol. 16, pp. 336–42.

Roozendaal, B., McEwen, B.S. and Chattarji, S. (2009) Stress, memory and the amygdala. *Nature Reviews Neuroscience*, vol. 10, pp. 423–33.

Ross, C.A. (2006) 'The sham ECT literature: implications for consent to ECT', *Ethical Human Psychology and Psychiatry*, vol. 8, pp. 17–28.

Royal College of Psychiatrists (2010) *Cognitive Behavioural Therapy (CBT)* [online], http://www.rcpsych.ac.uk/mentalhealthinformation/therapies/cognitivebehaviouraltherapy.aspx (Accessed May 2010).

Ruhé, H.G., Mason, N.S. and Schene, A.H. (2007) 'Mood is indirectly related to serotonin, norepinephrine and dopamine levels in humans: a meta-analysis of monoamine depletion studies', *Molecular Psychiatry*, vol. 12, pp. 331–59.

Russell, J.A. and Well, P.A. (1994) 'Predictors of happiness in married couples', *Personality and Individual Differences*, vol. 17, pp. 313–21.

Santarelli, L., Saxe, M., Gross, C., Surget, A., Battaglia, F., Dulawa, S. et al. (2003) 'Requirement of hippocampal neurogenesis for the behavioral effects of antidepressants', *Science*, vol. 301, no. 5634, pp. 805–9.

Sapolsky, R.M. (1998) *Why Zebras Don't Get Ulcers*, New York, Freeman.

Sapolsky, R.M. (2000) 'Glucocorticoids and hippocampal atrophy in neuropsychiatric disorders', *Archives of General Psychiatry*, vol. 57, pp. 925–35.

Schienle, A., Schäfer, A., Stark, R. and Vaitl, D. (2009) 'Long-term effects of cognitive behaviour therapy on brain activation in spider phobia', *Psychiatry Research: Neuroimaging*, vol. 172, pp. 99–102.

Schmuck, P. and Sheldon, K.M. (2001) 'Life goals and well-being: to the frontiers of life goal research', in Schmuck, P. and Sheldon, K.M. (eds) *Life Goals and Well-Being: Towards a Positive Psychology of Human Striving*, Kirkland, WA, US, Hogrefe and Huber Publishers.

Schwarz, N. (1990) 'Feelings as information: informational and motivational functions of affective states', in Higgins, E.T. and Sorrentino, R.M. (eds) *Handbook of Motivation and Cognition: Foundations of Social Behaviour*, New York, Guilford, pp. 527–61.

Schwarz, N. and Strack, F. (1991) 'Evaluating one's life: a judgement model of subjective well-being', in Strack, F., Argyle, M. and Schwarz, N. (eds) *Subjective Well-Being: An Interdisciplinary Perspective*, London, Pergamon Press, pp. 27–48.

Seligman, M. (2002) *Authentic Happiness*, New York, The Free Press.

Seligman, M. and Schulman, P. (1986) 'Explanatory style as a predictor of performance as a life insurance agent', *Journal of Personality and Social Psychology*, vol. 50, pp. 832–8.

Seligman, M.E.P. (1991) *Learned Optimism*, New York, Knopf.

Seligman, M.E.P. (1992 [1975]) *Helplessness: On Depression, Development, and Death*, San Francisco, W.H. Freeman.

Seligman, M.E.P. and Csikszentmihalyi, M. (2000) 'Positive psychology: an introduction', *American Psychologist*, vol. 55, pp. 5–14.

Seligman, M.E.P., Steen, T., Park, N. and Peterson, P. (2005) 'Positive psychology progress, empirical validation of interventions', *American Psychologist*, vol. 60, no. 5, pp. 410–21.

Selye, H. (1978 [1956]) *The Stress of Life* (2nd edn), New York, McGraw Hill.

Sen, S., Duman, R. and Sanacora, G. (2008) 'Serum brain-derived neurotrophic factor, depression, and antidepressant medications: meta-analyses and implications', *Biological Psychiatry*, vol. 64, pp. 527–32.

Shapiro, L.S. (2009) 'Meditation and positive psychology', in Lopez, S.J. (ed.) *Handbook of Positive Psychology* (2nd edn), Oxford, Oxford University Press, pp. 601–10.

Sin, N.L. and Lyubomirsky, S. (2009) 'Enhancing well-being and alleviating depressive symptoms with positive psychology interventions: a practice-friendly meta-analysis', *Journal of Clinical Psychology: In Session*, vol. 65, pp. 467–87.

Smoller, J.W., Gardner-Schuster, E. and Misiaszek, M. (2008) 'Genetics of anxiety: would the genome recognize the DSM?', *Depression and Anxiety*, vol. 25, pp. 368–77.

Stanley, M. and Mann, J.J. (1983) 'Increased serotonin-2 binding site in frontal cortex of suicide victims', *The Lancet*, vol. 1, pp. 214–16.

Stein, M.B. (1998) 'Neurobiological perspectives on social phobia: from affiliation to zoology', *Biological Psychiatry*, vol. 44, no. 12, pp. 1277–85.

Suh, E., Diener, E. and Fujuta, F. (1996) 'Events and subjective well-being: only recent events matter', *Journal of Personality and Social Psychology*, vol. 70, pp. 1091–2.

Sullivan, P.F., Neale, M.C. and Kendler, K.S. (2000) 'Genetic epidemiology of major depression: review and meta-analysis', *American Journal of Psychiatry*, vol. 157, pp. 1552–62.

Teasdale, J.D., Segal, Z.V., Williams, J.M.G., Ridgeway, V., Lau, M. and Soulsby, J. (2000) 'Reducing risk of recurrence of major depression using mindfulness-based cognitive therapy', *Journal of Consulting and Clinical Psychology*, vol. 68, pp. 615–23.

Tellegen, A., Lykken, D.T., Bouchard, T.J., Wilcox, K.J., Segal, N.L. and Rich, S. (1988) 'Personality similarity in twins reared apart and together', *Personality and Social Psychology*, vol. 54, pp. 1031–9.

Thayer, J.F., Friedman, B.H. and Borkovec, T.D. (1996) 'Autonomic characteristics of generalised anxiety disorder and worry', *Biological Psychiatry*, vol. 39, no. 4, pp. 255–66.

Thomas, C.M. and Morris, S. (2003) 'Cost of depression among adults in England in 2000', *The British Journal of Psychiatry*, vol. 183, pp. 514–19.

Toates, F. (2009) *Burrhus F. Skinner*, Palgrave Macmillan, Basingstoke.

Trut, L.N. (1999) 'Early canid domestication: the farm-fox experiment', *American Scientist*, vol. 87, pp. 160–9.

Tsankova, N.M., Berton, O., Renthal, W., Kumar, A., Neve, R.L. and Nestler, E.J. (2006) 'Sustained hippocampal chromatin regulation in a mouse model of depression and antidepressant action', *Nature Neuroscience*, vol. 9, no. 4, pp. 519–25.

Turner, R.J. and Lloyd, D.A. (1995) 'Lifetime trauma and mental health: the significance of cumulative adversity', *Journal of Health and Social Behavior*, vol. 36, pp. 360–76.

Twenge, J.M. (2006) *Generation Me*, New York: Simon and Schuster.

Twenge, J.M., Campbell, W.K. and Foster, C.A. (2003) 'Parenthood and marital satisfaction', *Journal of Marriage and Family*, vol. 65, no. 3, pp. 574–83.

Tyrer, P. (2001) 'The case for cothymia: mixed anxiety and depression as a single diagnosis', *The British Journal of Psychiatry*, vol. 179, pp. 191–3.

Tyrer, P. (2009) 'Are general practitioners really unable to diagnose depression?', *The Lancet*, vol. 374, pp. 589–90.

Van Deurzen, E. (2008) *Psychotherapy and the Quest for Happiness*, London, Sage Publications.

Veenhoven, R. (1991) 'Is happiness relative?', *Social Indicators Research*, vol. 24, pp. 1–34.

Veenhoven, R. (1994) *Correlates of Happiness* (3 vols), Rotterdam, the Netherlands, RISBO, Centre for Socio-Cultural Transformation.

Walker, C. (1977) 'Some variations in marital satisfaction', in Chester, R. and Peel, J. (eds) *Equalities and Inequalities and Family Life*, London, Academic Press, pp. 127–39.

Warner-Schmidt, J.L. and Duman, R.S. (2006) 'Hippocampal neurogenesis: opposing effects of stress and antidepressant treatment', *Hippocampus*, vol. 16, pp. 239–49.

Warr, P. (1999) 'Well-being and the workplace', in Kahneman, D., Diener, E. and Schwarz, N. (eds) *Well-being: The Foundations of Hedonic Psychology*, New York, Russell Sage, pp. 392–412.

Watson, D., Clark, L.A. and Tellegen, A. (1988) 'Development and validation of brief measures of positive and negative affect: the PANAS scales', *Journal of Personality and Social Psychology*, vol. 54, pp. 1063–70.

Weaver, I.C.G., Cervoni, N., Champagne, F.A., D'Alessio, A.C., Sharma, S., Seckl, J.R., Dymov, S., Szyf, M., Meaney, M.J., et al. (2004) 'Epigenetic programming by maternal behavior', *Nature Neuroscience*, vol. 7, pp. 847–54.

Weiss, E.L., Longhurst, J.G. and Mazure, C.M. (1999) 'Childhood sexual abuse as a risk factor for depression in women: Psychosocial and neurobiological correlates', *American Journal of Psychiatry*, vol. 156, pp. 816–28.

Weissman, M.M., Bland, R.C., Canino, G.J, et al. (1996) 'Cross-national epidemiology of major depression and bipolar disorder', *Journal of the American Medical Association*, vol. 276. no. 4, pp. 293–9.

Wheeler, L., Reis, H. and Nezlek, J. (1983) 'Loneliness, social interaction and social roles', *Journal of Personality and Social Psychology*, vol. 45, pp. 943–53.

Wilkinson, R. and Pickett, K. (2009) *The Spirit Level: Why More Equal Societies Almost Always Do Better*, London, Allen Lane.

Witvliet, C.V., Ludwig, T.E. and Vander Laan, K.L. (2001) 'Granting forgiveness or harboring grudges: implications for emotion, physiology, and health', *Psychological Science*, vol. 12, no. 2, pp. 117–23.

Wolpert, L. (2001) *Malignant Sadness: The Anatomy of Depression*, London, Faber and Faber.

Wolpert, L. (2009) 'Experiencing depression', in Pariante, C.M., Nesse, R.M., Nutt, D. and Wolpert, L. (eds) *Understanding Depression: A Translational Approach*, Oxford, Oxford University Press, pp. 1–5.

World Heath Organization (WHO) (2007) *The International Statistical Classification of Diseases and Related Health Problems*, (10th Revision) (ICD-10) Chapter V 'Mental and Behavioural Disorders' [online], http://apps.who.int/classifications/apps/icd/icd10online/ (Accessed June 2010).

Yates, M., Leake, A., Candy, J.M., Fairbairn, A.F., McKeith, I.G. and Ferrier, I.N. (1990) '5-HT2 receptor changes in major depression', *Biological Psychiatry*, vol. 27, pp. 489–96.

Acknowledgements

Grateful acknowledgement is made to Katherine Leys for coordinating the Research Methods boxes throughout SDK228.

Grateful acknowledgement is also made to the following sources:

Table

Table 1.1: Brown et al. (1995) 'Humiliation and Entrapment', Cambridge Journals.

Boxes

Box 3.2: © Royal College of Psychiatrists;

Box 4.4: © www.wellbeingwizard.com

Figures

Figure 1.1: © 2009 The Health and Social Care Information Centre, Social Care Statistics. All rights reserved; Figure 1.2a and 1.2b: © Publisher Unknown; Figure 1.6: © Pam Smit/Alamy; Figure 1.9: Adapted from Dickerson, S.S. and Kemeny, M.E. (2004) *Mean Cortisol Effect Size for Studies Using Passive Tasks*, American Psychological Association; Figure 1.10: Copyright © Antonia Reeve/Science Photo Library; Figure 1.11: © Richard Paisley/Doctor Stock/Getty Images; Figure 1.12: Hirschfield, R.M. A. (2001) 'The Comorbidity of Majory Depression and Anxiety Disorders: Recognition and Management in Primary Care', *Primary Care Companion to the Journal of Clinical Psychiatry*, Physicians Postgraduate Press Inc.; Figure 1.13: Das-Munshi, Jayati, et al. (2008) 'Public Health Significance of Mixed Anxierty and Depression: Beyond Current Classification', *British Journal of Psychiatry*, The Royal College of Psychiatrists; Figure 2.1a: © G&D Images/Alamy; Figure 2.1b: © Index Stock/Alamy; Figure 2.1c: © Nassar/XinHua/XinhuaPress/Corbis; Figure 2.1d: © Corbis Images; Figure 2.3: © Helm, C. et al. (2000) 'Pituitary-Adrenal and Autonomic Responses to Stress in Women after Sexual and Physical Abuse in Childhood', American Medical Association; Figure 2.4a: © Mike Dodd; Figures 2.4b and 2.4c: © Brian Hare; Figure 2.5: © Lupien, S.J. et al. (2009) 'Effects of Stress Throughout the Lifespan on the Brain, Behaviour and Cognition', Nature Publishing Group; Figure 2.6c: © Mitra, R. and Sapolsky, R.M. (2008) 'Acute Corticosterone Treatment is Sufficienty to Induce Anxiety And Amygdaloidal Dendrite Hypertrophy', *Proceedings of the National Academy of Science USA*; Figure 2.7: © Nitschke, et al. (2009) 'Anticipatory activation in the amygdale and anterior cingulated in generalized anxiety disorder and prediction of treatment response', *American Journal of Psychiatry*; Figure 2.8b: © Google Inc.; Figure 2.15: © Higgins, E.S. (2008) 'The New Genetics of Mental Illness', Scientific American Mind; Figure 3.2: © Bonanno, G.A. (2004) *Loss, Trauma and Human Resilience*, American Psychological Association; Figure 3.3: © Davey, G. (2008) 'NICE Stepped Care Model for Depression', *Psyopathology - Research, Assessment and*

Treatment in Clinical Psychology, John Wiley & Sons Limited; Figure 3.6: © Proudfoot, J. et al. (2004), 'Clinical Efficacy of Computerised Cognitive-Behavioural Therapy for Anxiety and Depression in Primary Care: Randomised Controlled Trial', *British Journal of Psychiatry*, Royal College of Psychiatrists; Figure 3.7: Adapted from DeRueis et al. (2008) 'Cognitive Therapy and Anti-depressant Medication Have Comparable Short-term Effects', Macmillan Publishing Company Inc.; Figure 3.8: © DeRubeis, R.J., Siegle, G.J. and Hollon, S.D. (2008) 'Cognitive Therapy Versus Medication for Depression: Treatment Outcomes and Neural Mechanisms', Macmillan Publishing Company Limited; Figure 3.10: © Southwest Neurosurgical Association; Figure 3.11: © Goldapple, K. et al. (2004) 'Modulation of Cortical-Limbic Pathways in Major Depression', Archives of General Psychiatry, American Medical Association; Figure 3.13a: © Pradeep Kumar/iStockphoto; Figure 3.13b: © Alexsandar Dickov; Figure 3.13c: © Bubbles Photolibrary/Alamy; Figure 3.13d: © Keith Ringland/Getty Images; Figures 3.14 and 3.15: © Ost, L.G. (2001) *Behaviour Research and Therapy*, Pergamon Press Plc; Figure 4.1: © Keystone/Stringer/Getty Images; Figure 4.2: Courtesy Google Inc; Figure 4.3: © Purestock/Alamy; Figure 4.4: © Anne Clark/iStockphoto.com; Figure 4.7: © David Gould/Getty Images; Figure 4.8: © Krings, E. et al. (2001) *Journal of Neurology, Neurosurgery and Psychiatry*, BMJ Publishing Group; Figure 4.9a: © digitalskillet/iStockphoto; Figure 4.9b: © Rex Features Limited; Figure 4.11: © Bruno De Hogues/Getty Images; Figure 4.13: © James Balston/Arcaid/Corbis; Figure 4.14: © Corbis Premium RF/Alamy; Figure 4.15: © Tim Teebken/Photodisc/Getty Images.

SDK228 Team

Claire Rostron (*SDK228 Chair and Academic Editor*)
Basiro Davey (*Advisor*)
Viki Burnage (*SDK228 Manager*)
Helen Copperwheat (*SDK228 Assistant*)
Frederick Toates (*Block 1 Chair*)
Antonio Martins-Mourao
Saroj Datta (*Block 2 Chair*)
Heather McLannahan (*SDK228 Deputy Chair*)
Ellie Dommett (*Block 3 Chair*)
Katherine Leys (*Block 4 Chair*)

Consultants

Ilona Boniwell
Christine Heading
Margaret Swithenby

External assessor

Professor Neil Frude

Critical readers

Meg Barker
Mick McCormick
Ulf Wagner

Developmental testers

Elena Gammage
Jen Evans
Vicky Gaeta

Production team

Greg Black
Ann Carter
Martin Chiverton
Roger Courthold
Rebecca Graham
Sara Hack
Nicky Heath
Chris Hough
Carol Houghton
Roger Moore
Jon Owen
Judith Pickering
Brian Richardson

Federica Sacco
Bina Sharma

Indexer

Jane Henley

Library

Duncan Belks

Index

Index entries and page numbers in **bold** are glossary terms. Page numbers in *italics* refer to figures or tables.